National 5 Chemistry

How to Pass

NATIONAL 5

Chemistry

Barry McBride

HODDER GIBSON
AN HACHETTE UK COMPANY

The Publishers would like to thank the following for permission to reproduce copyright material:

Photo credits:
p.19 (right) © W. Oelen, Courtesy of Wikipeida; p.19 (top left) © Martyn F. Chillmaid/Science Photo Library; p.19 (bottom left) © Pascal Goetgheluck/Science Photo Library; p.36 (left) © Kelpfish – Fotolia.com; p.36 (right) © Jack Star/Photodisc/Getty Images/Environmental Concerns 31; p.46 (left) © Koriolis – Fotolia.com; p.46 (right) © J. Marshall – Tribaleye Images/Alamy; p.50 (left) © Jim Parkin/Alamy; p.50 (right) © ranplett/iStockphoto.com; p.80 © Chris Mattison/Alamy.

Orders: please contact Bookpoint Ltd, 130 Park Drive, Abingdon, Oxon OX14 4SE. Telephone: (44) 01235 827720. Fax: (44) 01235 400454. Lines are open 9.00–5.00, Monday to Saturday, with a 24-hour message answering service. Visit our website at www.hoddereducation.co.uk. Hodder Gibson can be contacted direct on: Tel: 0141 848 1609; Fax: 0141 889 6315; email: hoddergibson@hodder.co.uk

First published in 2013 by
Hodder Gibson, an imprint of Hodder Education,
An Hachette UK Company
2a Christie Street
Paisley PA1 1NB

Impression number 5 4 3 2

Year 2017 2016 2015 2014 2013

Cover photo © Igor Kali – Fotolia
Illustrations by Emma Golley at Redmoor Design and Aptara, Inc.
Typeset in 13/15 Cronos Pro (Light) by Aptara, Inc.
Printed in Spain
A catalogue record for this title is available from the British Library
ISBN: 978 1444 181 982

Contents

Introduction

Students

To get the most from this book it is essential that it is read carefully and at a steady pace to allow you time to understand the concepts and theories. Throughout the book there are Hints and Tips and definitions that must be learned; pay particular attention to these as they will help greatly. Most importantly work hard, always do your best and good luck!

Teachers and parents

This book has been developed to cover all the mandatory content as outlined in the National 5 Chemistry Course Support Notes. It also contains some National 4 content to refresh students' knowledge before progressing further into the topic. It is intended to be accessible to students and deliver concepts and theories in a 'straight to the point' manner using clear and simple language. It can be used as a classroom aid and for students' personal study and is full of helpful hints and proven classroom methods of delivering difficult concepts in a style that students can relate to and understand.

Exam details

The final exam paper will have two sections.

- Section A will contain objective questions (multiple choice) and will have 20 marks.
- Section B will contain restricted and extended response questions and will have 60 marks.

The majority of the marks will be awarded for demonstrating and applying knowledge and understanding of the mandatory content of the Course. The other marks will be awarded for applying scientific inquiry skills. Marks will be distributed approximately proportionately across the three Units.

There will be several question types in the exam paper including:

- Extended response questions – explaining a concept for example
- Open-ended questions
- Making accurate statements
- Calculations

Unit Assessment

Candidates will also have to complete an assessment at the end of each unit. This assessment will be produced by the school/college. Most centres will produce a set of questions that are similar to those found in the National 5 exam papers. Candidates must also complete two additional assessments tasks.

Assessment Task 1 – This assessment task requires candidates to apply skills of scientific inquiry to carry out an experiment that draws on knowledge and understanding of the key areas of the unit and to produce a report on the experiment that provides evidence that the candidate has planned an experiment, recorded observations/measurements accurately, presented results in an appropriate format, drawn valid conclusions and evaluated experimental procedures.

Assessment Task 2 – This assessment task requires candidates to apply scientific skills by carrying out a number of investigations associated with the key areas of the unit. The candidate should select an application of chemistry from a key area within the unit which they will investigate. This may be via textbooks, resource packs, internet, visits to appropriate facilities or any other suitable approach. The candidate should also consider the impact of this application on the environment/society.

Unit 1 Chemical Changes and Structure

Chapter 1.1
Rates of Reaction

Chemical reactions can take place in less than a second in an explosion, or they can be very slow like the corrosion of iron. In this section we will revise the factors that affect the rate of chemical reactions and how the rate of a reaction can be calculated.

There are several factors that affect the rate of a chemical reaction:

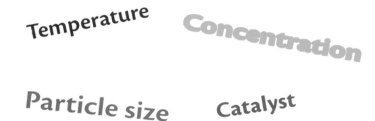

Particle size **Catalyst**

To understand how they affect the rate of a reaction we must first think about why reactions happen. For a reaction to take place, **particles** must collide and combine to form new products.

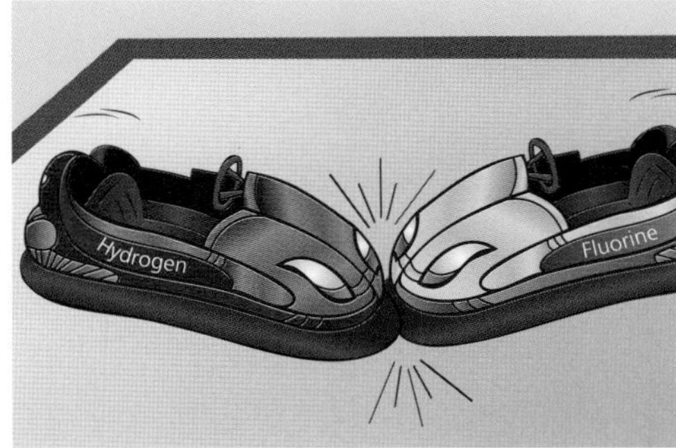

Figure 1.1

Temperature

- The higher the temperature, the faster the reaction.
- The lower the temperature, the slower the reaction.

Increasing the temperature increases the energy of the particles making them move faster and so more successful collisions can occur.

Figure 1.2

Concentration

- The higher the concentration, the faster the reaction.
- The lower the concentration, the slower the reaction.

If the concentration is increased, there are more **atoms** present, and as a result more collisions take place.

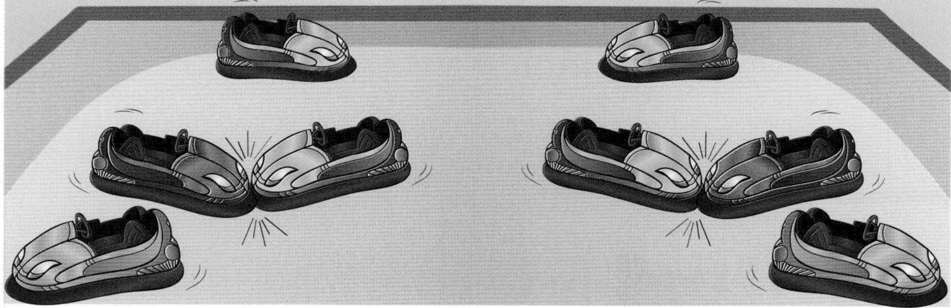

Figure 1.3

Particle size

If the particle size is reduced (the reactants are broken into smaller pieces), then the rate of the reaction is increased. This is because a small particle size results in a large surface area meaning that collisions will happen more frequently.

Key points

- The smaller the particle size the faster the reaction.
- The larger the particle size the slower the reaction.

Catalysts

* Catalysts alter the rate of a reaction but are not used up in the reaction.
* Most catalysts increase the rate of a chemical reaction.

Catalysts are used a lot in industry as they allow reactions to be performed at a lower temperature, which saves energy and money. They also increase the rate of the reaction. Platinum and other transition metals are used in car exhaust systems to convert harmful gases into less harmful gases.

There are two main types of catalyst:

- **Homogeneous catalyst** – is in the same state as the reactants. These are available in all states.
- **Heterogeneous catalyst** – is in a different state from the reactants. These are usually only available in the solid state.

Heterogeneous catalysts work by the method of **adsorption**. (Yes, adsorption not absorption!)

1. The reactant molecules are adsorbed onto the active sites of the catalyst. The bonds inside the molecules start to break (Figure 1.4).
2. The molecules are held at a favourable angle so that reactions can occur (Figure 1.5).
3. Product molecules are free to leave the catalyst in a stage called desorption (Figure 1.6). The surface of the catalyst is left unchanged.

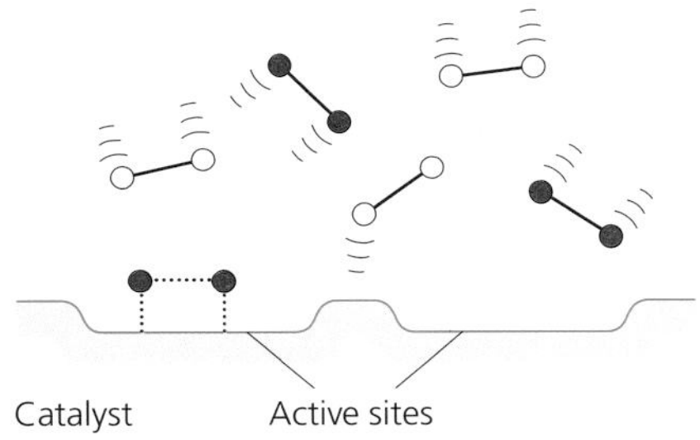

Figure 1.4 Adsorption

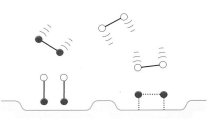

Figure 1.5 Reaction

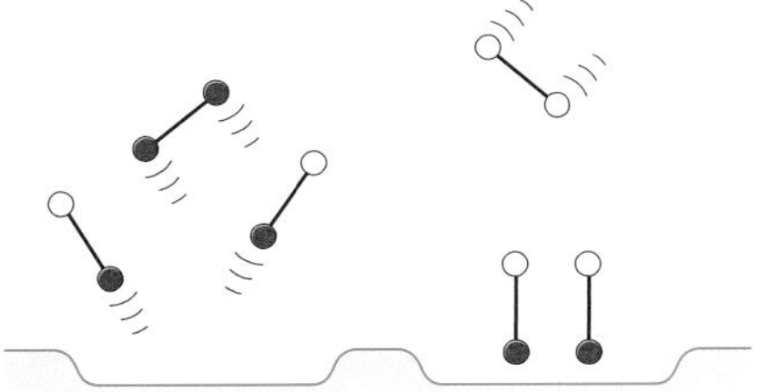

Figure 1.6 Desorption

Catalysts are also found in nature. **Enzymes** are biological catalysts and are used within the body, such as amylase in saliva (an example of homogeneous catalysis), but can also be used in processes such as the **fermentation** of sugars to produce alcohol.

Remember

Variable	Effect on reaction rate	Example
Temperature	Low temperature = slow reaction High temperature = fast reaction	If food is kept in the fridge, the reactions that cause the food to go off are slowed down allowing the food to last longer.
Concentration	Low concentration = slow reaction High concentration = fast reaction	Chalk will react much faster with a more concentrated acid.
Particle size	Small particle size = fast reaction Large particle size = slow reaction	Chips cook much faster than whole potatoes because chips have a larger surface area due to their smaller particle size.
Catalyst	Catalysts alter the rate of a reaction but are not used in a reaction	In the Haber process (see page 72) an iron catalyst is used to allow the production of ammonia to take place at a lower temperature.

Following the course of a reaction

In chemistry, many measurements can be taken to follow the course of a reaction. The two most common ways of monitoring a reaction are measuring the volume of gas produced and measuring the loss in mass over a period of time. These measurements allow us to produce rate graphs that tell us many things about a reaction.

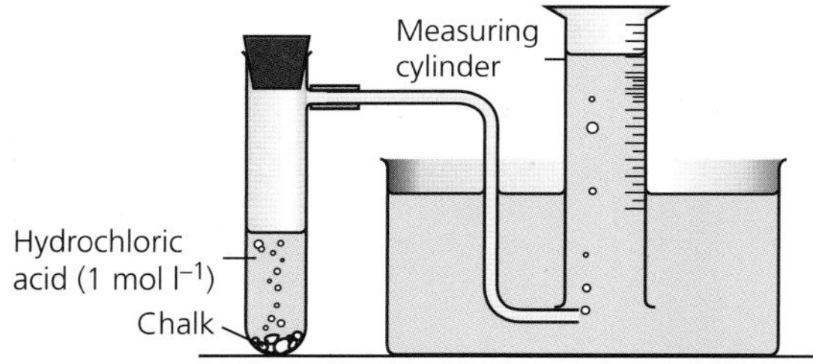

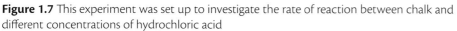

Figure 1.7 This experiment was set up to investigate the rate of reaction between chalk and different concentrations of hydrochloric acid

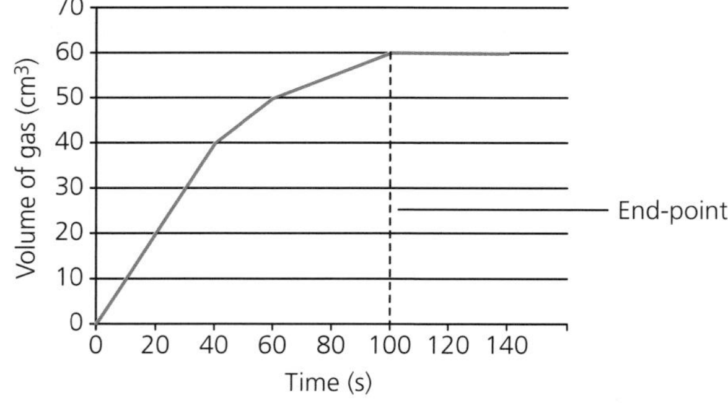

Figure 1.8 The volume of gas collected in Figure 1.7 was recorded every 20 seconds, and when the reaction was complete this graph was drawn

Hints & tips

Note the units for the rate – the volume is given in cm^3 and the time in seconds so the rate is $cm^3 s^{-1}$.

The point on the graph when the line becomes flat (horizontal) is called the end-point (shown by the dotted line). This is because there is no longer any gas being produced, therefore the reaction has stopped. Generally the rate of a reaction slows as it progresses because the reactants are being used up.

Rate graphs can be used to calculate the rate of the reaction using the following equation:

$$\textbf{rate} = \frac{\textbf{change in volume or mass}}{\textbf{change in time}}$$

Example

1 Calculate the rate of reaction for the first 60 seconds of the reaction shown in Figure 1.8.

Answer: *In the first 60 seconds of the reaction the volume changes from 0 to 50 cm³.*

$$rate = \frac{50}{60} = 0.83\ cm^3s^{-1}$$

The reaction was repeated using a higher concentration of **acid** and the results were drawn onto the same graph (Figure 1.9).

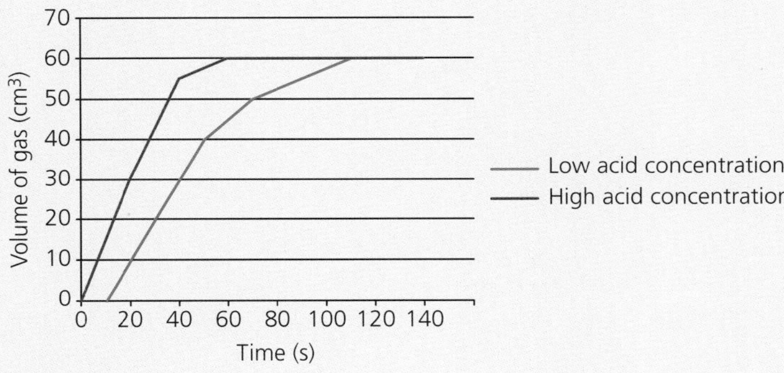

Figure 1.9

The rates of the two reactions can be compared by using the previous calculation.

2 Calculate the rate of reaction for the first 60 seconds of reaction 2.

Answer: *In the first 60 seconds of the reaction the volume changes from 0 to 60 cm³.*

$$rate = \frac{60}{60} = 1\ cm^3s^{-1}$$

The rate of the second reaction is higher because the concentration of acid has been increased. This can also be seen from the graph (Figure 1.9), as the end-point of reaction 2 is reached before the end-point of reaction 1.

Study questions ?

1 A reaction between acid and chalk was carried out to monitor the rate of reaction. Which of the following changes would not affect the rate of the reaction?

A Change in size of test tube
B Change in particle size of chalk
C Change in concentration of acid
D Change in temperature of the acid

2 The decomposition of hydrogen peroxide is catalysed by manganese dioxide. If 10 g of manganese dioxide is added to the hydrogen peroxide, what mass of manganese dioxide can be recovered after the reaction is complete?

A 0 g
B 5 g
C 10 g
D 20 g

3 John and Grace were investigating the rate of reaction between 3 g of chalk and 1 mol l^{-1} hydrochloric acid. They monitored the reaction by measuring the volume of carbon dioxide gas produced over time.

a) Complete Figure 1.10 showing how a sample of the gas could be collected.

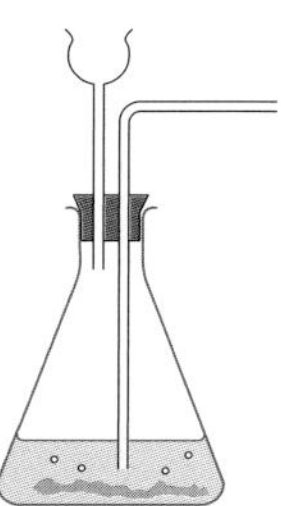

Figure 1.10

Time (s)	Volume of CO_2 (cm^3)
0	0
10	10
20	20
30	28
40	35
50	41
60	45
70	48
80	50
90	51
100	51

b) The table above shows the results obtained. Draw a line graph to show these results.
c) Calculate the rate of reaction for the first 40 seconds.
d) Why does the rate of the reaction slow as time proceeds?
e) At what time after the start did the reaction finish?
f) The reaction was repeated with a higher concentration of acid. Draw a line on the graph to represent the results that you would expect for this experiment.

4 In industry, catalysts are often used to increase productivity. The catalysts used are usually in the form of a fine powder. Suggest why the catalysts are used in this form rather than as a lump.

5 The effectiveness of enzymes in catalysing the decomposition of hydrogen peroxide was investigated. A piece of liver was added to one test tube of hydrogen peroxide and the volume of oxygen gas recorded (see Figure 1.11). This experiment was repeated with a piece of potato. The results obtained are shown in Figure 1.12.

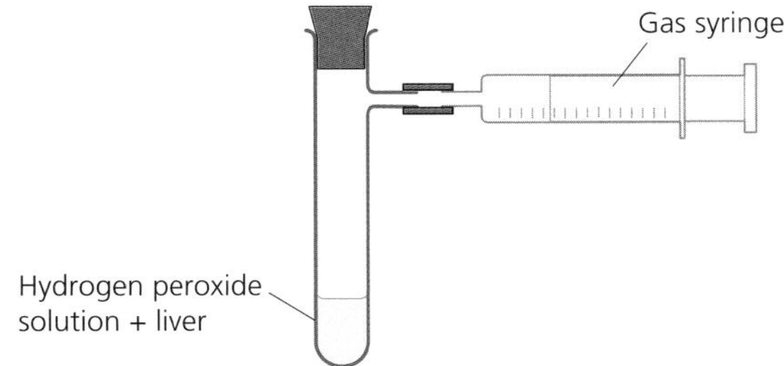

Figure 1.11

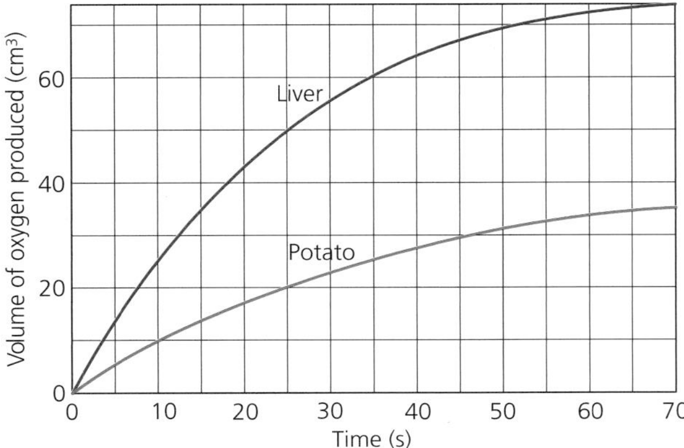

Figure 1.12

a) Calculate the rate of reaction for the two experiments over the first 20 seconds.
b) Which of the two, liver or potato, contained the most effective enzyme for this reaction?
c) What factors had to be kept constant to ensure the results are valid?

Chapter 1.2 Atomic Theory

Everything is made of elements but if we could look very closely at an element, we would see that an element is made of very tiny particles called atoms. In this section we will revise what makes up the atom and what holds atoms together.

The atom

Before we can fully understand what holds atoms together it is important to look at the structure of the atom. Atoms are made up of three smaller particles:

1 **Electrons** Negatively charged particles that spin around the positive centre of the atom in circles called energy levels. (Imagine how the Moon spins around the Earth.) Their mass is so small it is nearly zero.

2 **Protons** Positively charged particles that are contained in the **nucleus** of the atom (the centre). They have a relative mass of 1.

3 **Neutrons** Neutrons are also contained in the nucleus of the atom but have no charge. They also have a relative mass of 1.

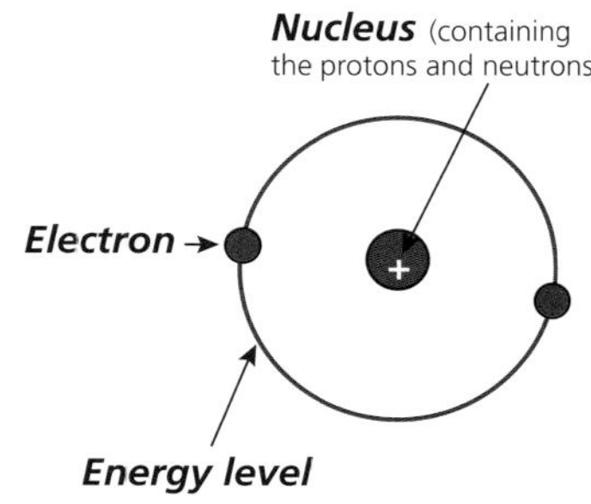

Figure 1.13 The atom

The nucleus has an overall positive charge because it contains all the protons. Atoms have no overall charge because they contain equal numbers of positive protons and negative electrons. These opposite charges cancel each other out making the atom neutral.

Remember

Particle	Mass	Charge	Location
Electron	Approx. 0	Negative	Energy level
Proton	1	Positive	Nucleus
Neutron	1	No charge	Nucleus

Electrons

Elements are arranged in the periodic table in order of increasing **atomic number**. For example hydrogen has the atomic number of 1, helium 2, lithium 3 and so on. The atomic number gives the number of protons in an atom. From this, the number of electrons can be worked out.

The atomic number of an element tells you how many protons an atom of that element has.

Example

The element shown in Figure 1.14 is sodium. The atomic number shows each atom of sodium has 11 protons. Because atoms are neutral, it must also have 11 electrons to cancel out the 11 protons.

Atomic number → $_{11}$Na

Figure 1.14

As you learned previously, the electrons that surround nuclei are contained in energy levels. These energy levels can only hold a certain amount of electrons. The first energy level (the one nearest the nucleus) can hold a maximum of two electrons with the others being able to hold up to a maximum of eight electrons. (This is only true for the first twenty elements.) This information allows us to draw a diagram of an atom showing how the electrons are arranged. (The electron arrangements of all atoms can be found in the data booklet.)

Example

Sodium has 11 electrons and the electron arrangement 2, 8, 1 so two go into the first energy level (the one nearest the nucleus). Eight go in the second energy level which leaves one that must go into the outer energy level.

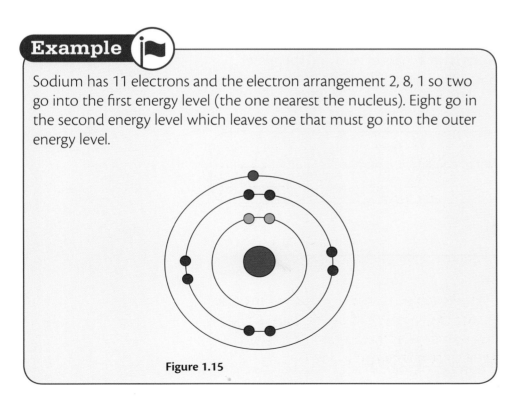

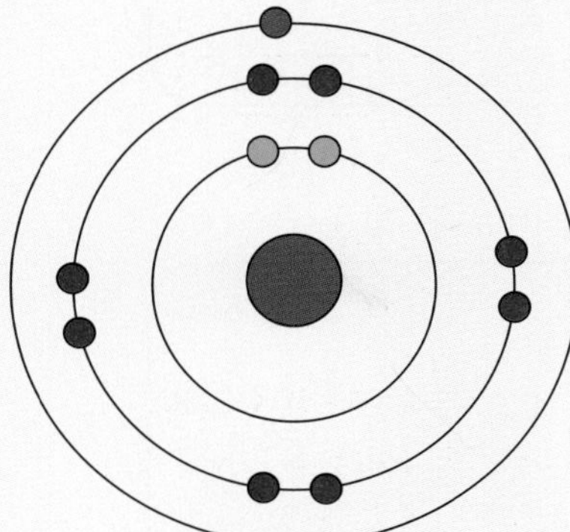

Figure 1.15

Hints & tips

To practise, draw the structure of each atom for the first twenty elements using the electron arrangements in your data booklet.

Elements in the same group of the periodic table react in very similar ways. This is because they all have the same number of outer electrons. All the **alkali metals** for example have one outer electron. This makes them all very reactive.

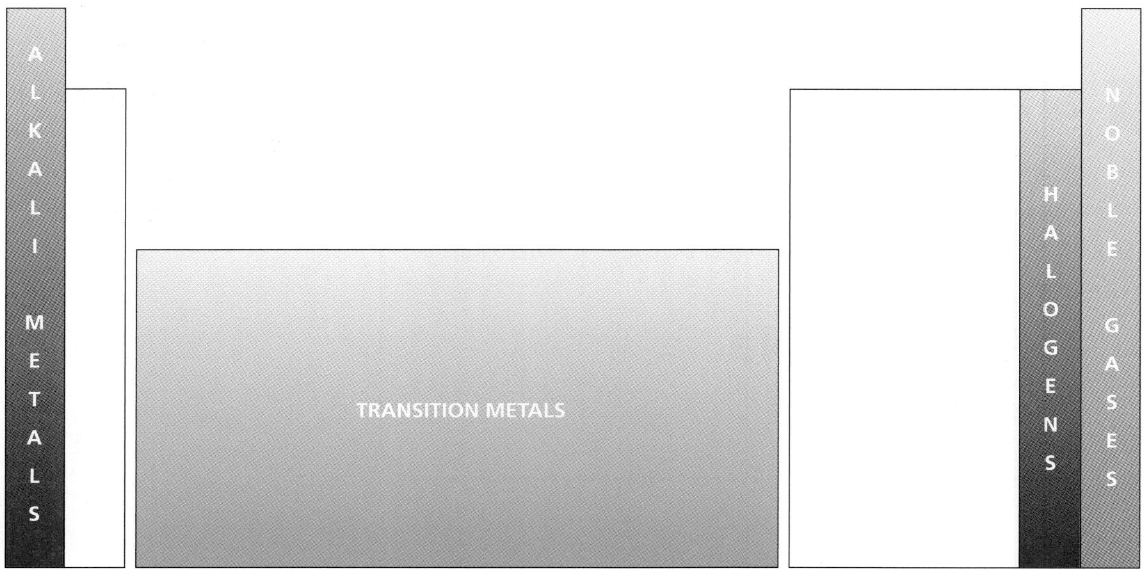

Figure 1.16 Groups in the periodic table.

Neutrons

We have seen how we use the atomic number to calculate the number of protons and electrons in an atom. We must also be able to work out how many neutrons there are in the nucleus of an atom.

To do this we need the **mass number** of the atom. The mass number is given in the top left of the element's symbol. To find out the number of neutrons, the number of protons needs to be deducted from the mass number. Remember that electrons have a mass of zero and therefore don't affect the mass of an atom.

The mass number of an element is equal to the number of protons plus the number of neutrons.

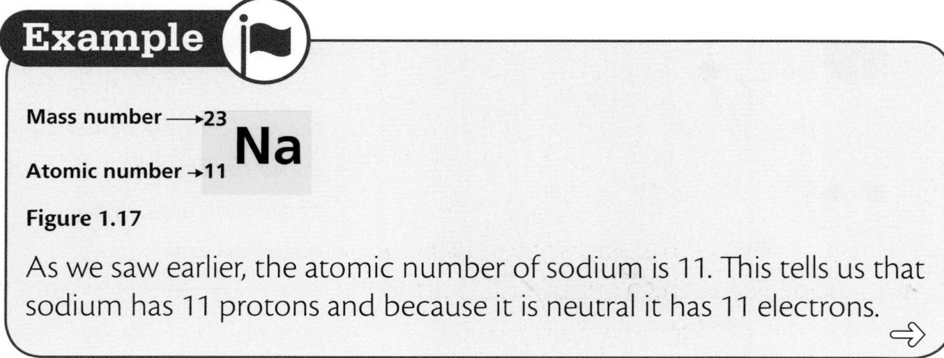

Example

Mass number → 23
Atomic number → 11
$^{23}_{11}Na$

Figure 1.17

As we saw earlier, the atomic number of sodium is 11. This tells us that sodium has 11 protons and because it is neutral it has 11 electrons.

The mass number of sodium is 23. So we can now work out the number of neutrons.

Total mass of sodium = 23

Mass of protons = 11

Mass of electrons = 0 (electrons have no mass)

Mass of neutrons = 12 (23 − 11 protons = 12 neutrons)

Some more examples are shown in the table below.

Element	Atomic number	Mass number	Number of protons	Number of electrons	Number of neutrons
Magnesium	12	24	12	12	12
Potassium	19	39	19	19	20
Carbon	6	12	6	6	6

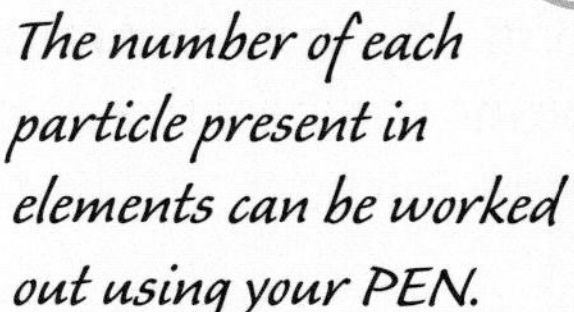

The number of each particle present in elements can be worked out using your PEN.

Protons Electrons Neutrons!

$^{19}_{9}F$ P = 9, E = 9, N = 10 (19 − 9)

Isotopes

The masses of the atoms of an element are not always the same. Just like people, atoms all have slightly different weights.

For example $^{12}_{6}C$ and $^{13}_{6}C$ are both carbon atoms.

They are **isotopes**; they have the same number of protons but the number of neutrons in each is different.

Key points

Isotopes are atoms with the same atomic number but different mass numbers.

Elements are made up of isotopes so the mass given in the data booklet is called the **relative atomic mass** (RAM), which is an average mass of all the isotopes of a single element.

The RAM can be used to give an indication of the relative abundance of isotopes in a sample.

Example

Copper has two isotopes:

$^{63}_{29}Cu$ and $^{65}_{29}Cu$.

The RAM of copper is 63.5.

The RAM indicates that copper-63 is the most abundant isotope due to the fact that the 63.5 is closer to copper-63 than to copper-65.

Ions

Atoms are neutral because they have an equal number of positive protons and negative electrons, but what happens when the numbers of positive protons and negative electrons in a particle are not equal?

When there is an imbalance of electrons to protons an **ion** is formed.

* An ion is a charged particle and they are formed when an atom gains or loses electrons.
* Metal atoms lose electrons to form positive ions and non-metal atoms gain electrons to form negative ions.

The reason that atoms gain or lose electrons is because of the **noble gases**. The noble gases are like the pop stars, movie stars or sport stars of our world. All elements in the periodic table want to be like them in every way! This is why noble gases won't react because they don't want to be changed at all. In chemistry terms they are said to be stable.

Key points !

The noble gases have a stable electron arrangement.

If other elements are to be like their heroes, they must try to achieve the same electron arrangement as a noble gas, which has a full outer energy level. Neon, for example, has eight outer electrons, whereas oxygen only has six outer electrons. To become stable like a noble gas, oxygen must gain two electrons from another atom.

Metals	Non-metals
Magnesium	**Chlorine**
Magnesium has the electron arrangement of 2, 8, 2. Being a metal it will lose 2 electrons to achieve the same electron arrangement as neon: 2, 8. $Mg \rightarrow Mg^{2+} + 2e^-$ This change creates an imbalance in the electron to proton ratio. $P = 12$ ${}^{24}_{12}Mg^{2+}$ $E = 10$ $N = 12$	Chlorine has the electron arrangement of 2, 8, 7. Being a non-metal it will gain 1 electron to achieve the same electron arrangement as argon: 2, 8, 8. $Cl + e^- \rightarrow Cl^-$ This change creates an imbalance in the electron to proton ratio. $P = 17$ ${}^{35}_{17}Cl^-$ $E = 18$ $N = 18$

This wee joke will test to see how well you understand ions!

I think I may have lost an electron.
Are you sure?
Aye am positive.

Study questions ?

1 Isotopes of an element have different:

A mass numbers **B** atomic numbers

C numbers of protons **D** numbers of electrons

2 An element has an atomic number of 11 and a mass number of 23. How many electrons are there in its atoms?

A 11 **B** 12 **C** 22 **D** 23

3 Which of the following electron arrangements is that of an element which has similar chemical properties to calcium?

A 2, 8, 1 **B** 2, 8, 2 **C** 2, 8, 3 **D** 2, 8, 4

4 Different atoms of the same element have identical:

A nuclei **B** mass numbers

C atomic numbers **D** numbers of neutrons

5 The nuclide notation can be used to work out the numbers of protons, neutrons and electrons that an ion contains. The nuclide notation of a silver ion is $^{107}_{47}Ag^{+}$.

a) Complete the table to show the number of each particle that this ion contains.

Particles	Number
Protons	
Electrons	
Neutrons	

b) A sample of silver is found to contain two atoms of silver with different masses: 107Ag and 109Ag. What name is given to atoms with different masses?

c) The relative atomic mass of silver is 108. What does this suggest about the relative abundance of these different atoms?

6 The nuclide notation shows the atomic number and mass number of an isotope. The nuclide notation for an isotope of neon is $^{21}_{10}Ne$.

a) An isotope of calcium has the atomic number of 20 and a mass number of 41. Write the nuclide notation for this isotope of calcium.

b) How many protons and neutrons does this isotope contain?

c) All the isotopes of calcium are electrically neutral. What does this suggest about the proton to electron ratio of each isotope?

Chapter 1.3
Bonding

Now that we have revised what an atom is, we now have to revise how these atoms combine and what holds them together to form compounds. In this section we will revise the different types of bond that form to join atoms together.

Molecules

A **molecule** is two or more atoms joined together by **covalent bonds** (see below). A molecule is usually made up of non-metal atoms only.

Water (H_2O) is an example of a molecule. It has two hydrogen atoms and one oxygen atom all held together by bonds.

Figure 1.18 A molecule of water

Covalent bonds

All elements in the periodic table want to be like a noble gas (see page 12) and have a full outer energy level. For example, neon has eight outer electrons whereas oxygen only has six outer electrons so to become stable like a noble gas it must gain two electrons. Hydrogen has only one outer electron and will gain one more to achieve the same arrangement as helium.

To do this, the element has to form bonds. The bonds formed are called covalent bonds.

Key points !

* A molecule is two or more atoms held together by covalent bonds.
* A covalent bond is a shared pair of electrons between two non-metal atoms.

The atoms are held together because of the electrostatic force of attraction between the positive nuclei of each atom and the negatively charged electrons. This is better illustrated as a diagram – see Figure 1.19.

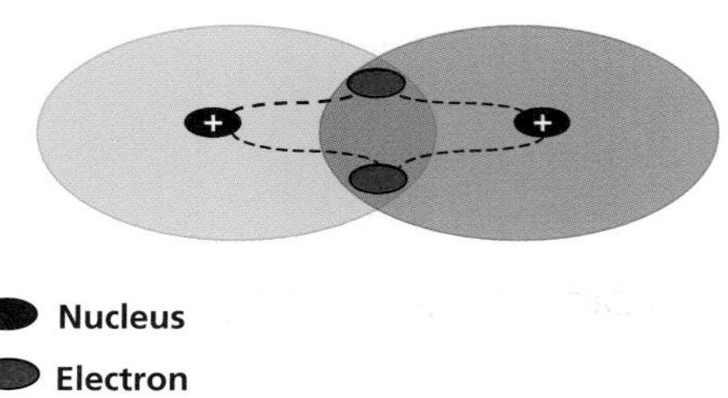

Nucleus
Electron

Figure 1.19 A molecule of hydrogen

The saying 'opposites attract' can be used to describe how a covalent bond works. The positively charged nucleus is attracted to the negatively charged electrons. However, the nucleus on the other side is also attracted to them. This creates a 'tug-of-war' effect. Both nuclei try to pull the electrons toward themselves creating a strong bond that holds the atoms together. This is shown by the dashed lines in Figure 1.19.

The diagram shown in Figure 1.19 is a molecule of hydrogen. Hydrogen has the electron arrangement of one. So by sharing electrons with another hydrogen atom, they both have two outer electrons. This results in them having the same electron arrangement as the noble gas, helium.

Hints & tips

Remember the 'tug-of-war' description, it will help you to describe exactly how a covalent bond holds the atoms together.

Diatomic elements

Hydrogen is classed as a **diatomic element** because it exists not as a single atom of hydrogen but as a pair of hydrogen atoms that share electrons to become stable. There are other elements in the periodic table that are also diatomic. In other words, they exist as pairs rather than single atoms. For example, oxygen is a diatomic molecule; that is why its formula is O_2. It is important to learn all seven diatomic elements.

Key points

A diatomic element is made up of molecules that contain two atoms.

Hints & tips

To make it easy to remember all the diatomic elements use this little mnemonic. Try it. It makes it very easy. Or make up your own.

Fancy	*Fluorine*	F_2
Clancy	*Chlorine*	Cl_2
Owes	*Oxygen*	O_2
Him	*Hydrogen*	H_2
Nothing	*Nitrogen*	N_2
But	*Bromine*	Br_2
Ice	*Iodine*	I_2

For all of the diatomic elements it is essential that you can draw a diagram of the molecule showing all of the outer electrons, like the example drawn for hydrogen in Figure 1.19.

Example

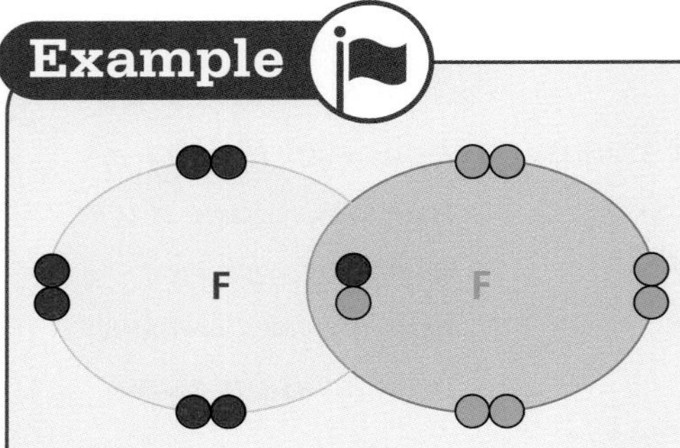

Figure 1.20 Fluorine 2, 7

Figure 1.20 shows a molecule of fluorine. An atom of fluorine requires one electron to become stable, therefore it will share one electron with another atom of fluorine to form two stable atoms.

Example

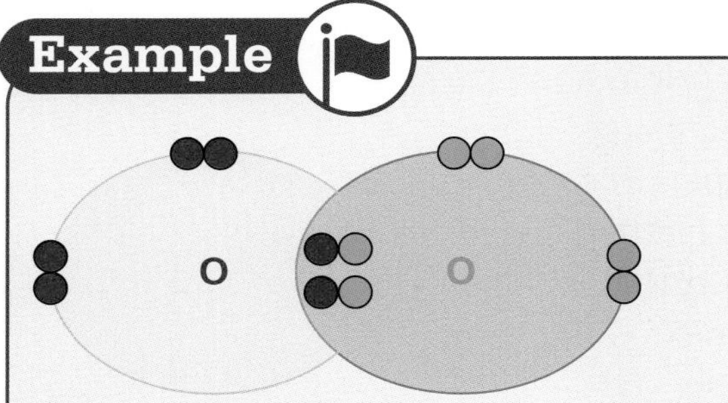

Figure 1.21 Oxygen 2, 6

Figure 1.21 shows a molecule of oxygen. Oxygen has the electron arrangement 2, 6 and requires two electrons to become stable. Because of this it must share two electrons with another oxygen atom. This means that oxygen forms a double covalent bond.

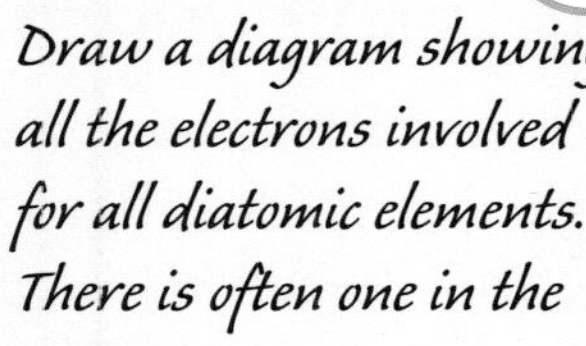

Hints & tips

Draw a diagram showing all the electrons involved for all diatomic elements. There is often one in the exam.

To make sure you have drawn the diagrams correctly just count the electrons. Each atom should have eight, except for hydrogen which should only have two. If they don't, try it again.

Covalent compounds

You may have noticed that so far we have only looked at how the bonds are formed in molecules of elements, but the same rules apply when dealing with the bonding in covalent **compounds**.

Example

Methane (carbon hydride) has the chemical formula of CH_4. This formula occurs because the atoms of carbon and hydrogen share electrons to become stable.

1 An atom of carbon has four outer electrons and therefore requires a further four to achieve a stable electron arrangement like a noble gas.

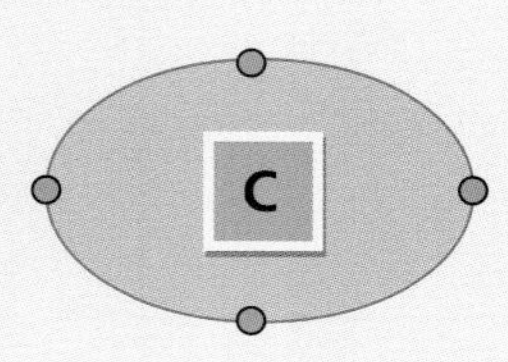

2 Hydrogen has only one outer electron and therefore requires only one more electron to achieve a stable electron arrangement.

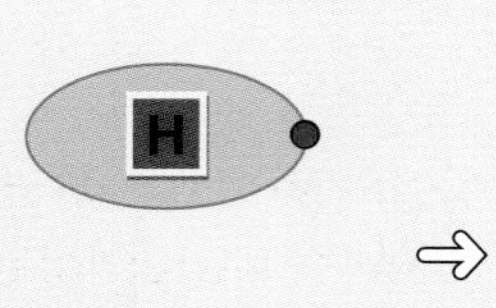

⇨

3 For the two to combine and form a stable compound in which both hydrogen and carbon have stable electron arrangements, the carbon atom requires four hydrogen atoms to supply the four electrons.

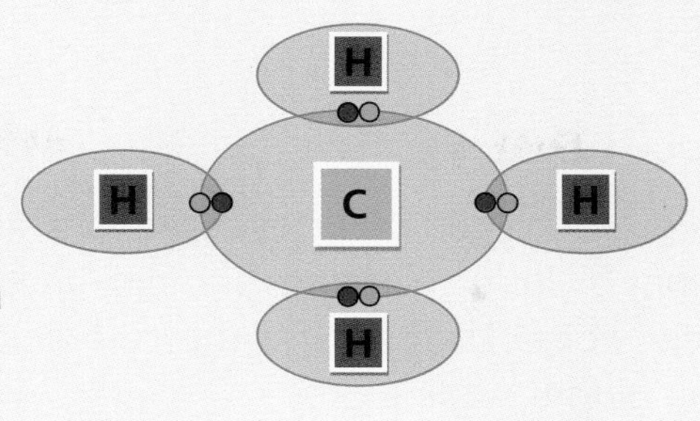

Sharing electrons in this way allows both hydrogen and carbon to have stable electron arrangements and this is the reason why methane (carbon hydride) has the formula of CH_4.

Shapes of molecules

The bonds that are formed also give the molecules a distinctive shape.

The shapes are caused by the repulsion of electrons that are in the bonds. Particles with the same charge move away from each other. So the electrons in a covalent bond repel the electrons in other covalent bonds causing them to move as far away from each other as possible. This creates molecules with different shapes.

Tetrahedral molecules

Methane (CH_4) is an example of a tetrahedral shaped molecule.

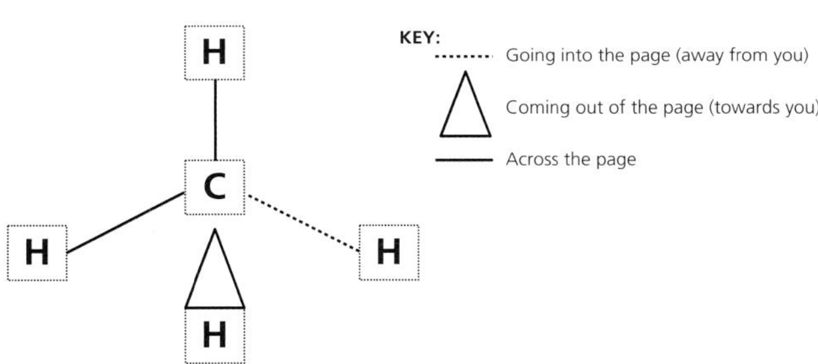

Figure 1.22 Methane (CH_4) – a tetrahedral shaped molecule

Linear molecules

Hydrogen fluoride (HF) is an example of a linear molecule.

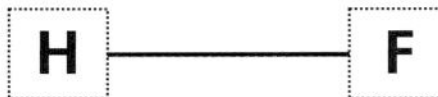

Figure 1.23 Hydrogen fluoride (HF) – a linear shaped molecule

Pyramidal molecules

Ammonia (NH_3) is an example of a pyramidal shaped molecule.

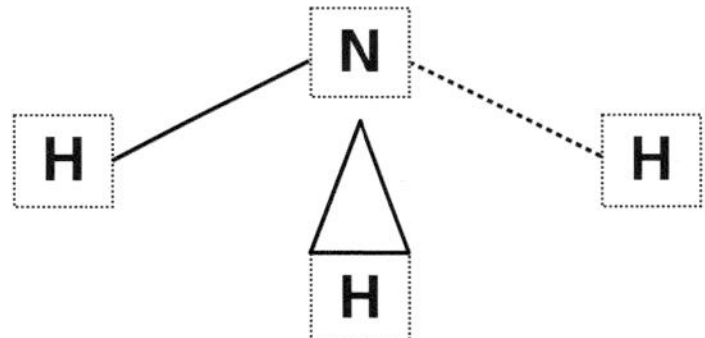

Figure 1.24 Ammonia (NH_3) – a pyramidal shaped molecule

Bent molecules

Water (H_2O) is an example of a bent shaped molecule.

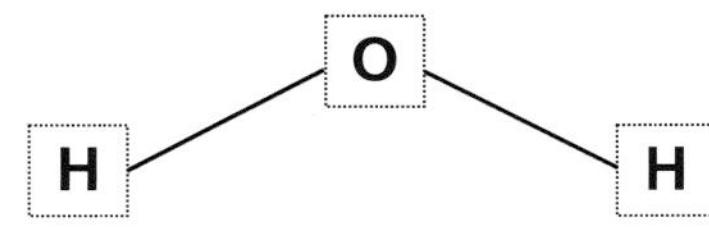

Figure 1.25 Water (H_2O) – a bent shaped molecule

All molecules that have a formula like methane will have the same shape, for example CCl_4 (carbon tetrachloride) will also be tetrahedral in shape.

Ionic bonding (opposites attract!)

In the previous section we looked at charged particles called ions, and the fact that metals form positive ions by losing electrons and non-metals form negative ions by gaining electrons. (Look back at the Ions section on page 12 to refresh your memory before reading on.)

The saying 'opposites attract' can be used to describe an **ionic bond**. The attraction between oppositely charged particles is called an electrostatic attraction.

Key points

An ionic bond is an electrostatic force of attraction between a positive metal ion and a negative non-metal ion.

The bonding present between atoms has a major impact on the properties of that substance. We will revise properties in the next section.

Study questions

Go to page 21, where you will find questions on bonding.

Chapter 1.4
Properties

The properties of a substance depend on the types of bonds that hold its atoms together. In this section we will revise how bonding affects the properties of a substance.

Ionic compounds

Ionic compounds form what is known as a lattice structure. This is a regular arrangement of metal and non-metal ions.

Figure 1.26 is a diagram of an **ionic lattice**. It is a cube-like structure. If you take a simple grain of salt and look at it very closely, you will see that the grain is a cube.

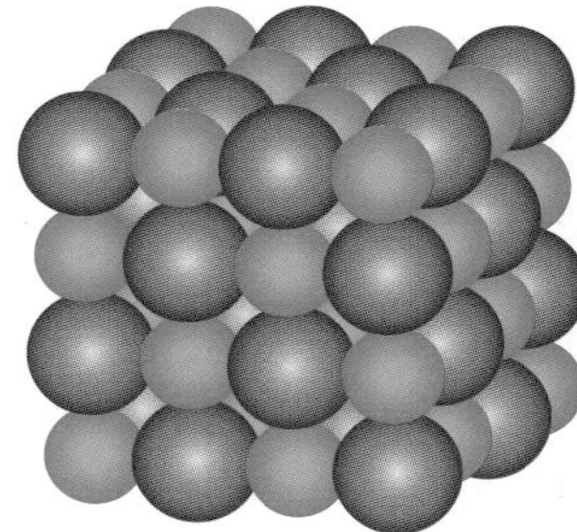

Figure 1.26 An ionic lattice structure

A lattice structure creates compounds with a high melting point which conduct when molten or in solution but NEVER when solid.

Ionic compounds dissolve in water easily. When they do this their lattice breaks up completely to form free ions. This enables them to conduct electricity as the ions are free to carry the electrical charge. They also have a high melting point because to melt an ionic compound the millions upon millions of strong ionic bonds must be broken and this requires lots of energy.

Not all ionic compounds form cube-like structures and a variety of shapes can be created from ionic crystals as can be seen in these photographs.

Figure 1.27 Sodium chloride

Figure 1.28 Lead chromate

Figure 1.29 Nickel sulphate

Covalent substances

There are two types of covalent substances:

- covalent network substances
- covalent molecular substances.

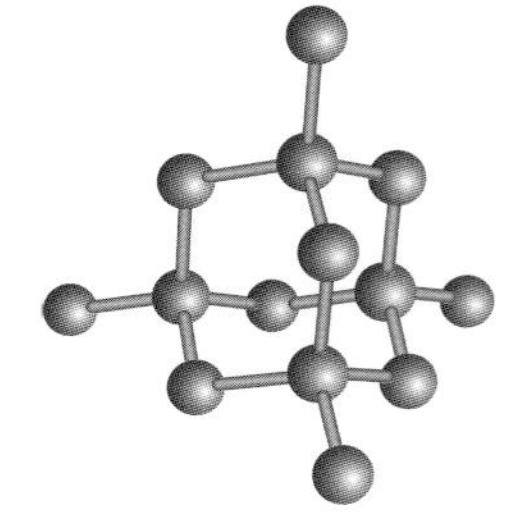

Figure 1.30 The covalent network structure of diamond

Covalent network substances have very high melting points and are very hard. Diamond for example is a covalent network structure made of carbon atoms and is used in cutting tools for cutting through rock.

The many carbon atoms are held together by strong covalent bonds which give diamond the properties of being very hard as well as having a very high melting point.

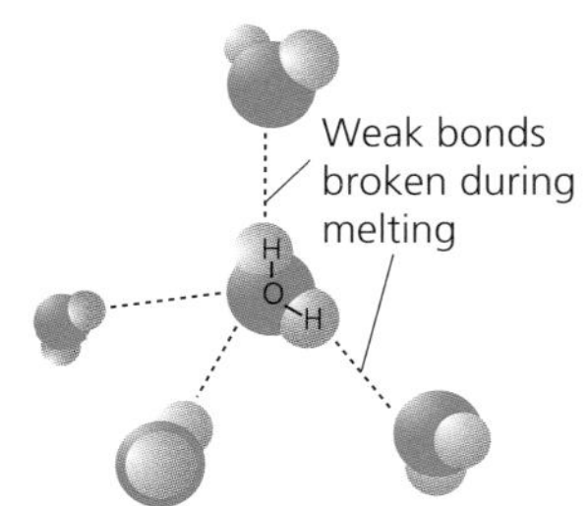

Figure 1.31 Weak bonds between molecules are broken when covalent molecular substances are melted

Covalent molecules such as oxygen and water all have low melting points and boiling points. This means that they are a liquid, gas or low melting point solid at room temperature. Like all covalent compounds they do not conduct electricity in any state, water being the only exception to this rule.

When a substance such as ice is melted, it is only the weak bonds between the molecules and not the strong covalent bonds that are broken.

There are always exceptions to these rules of bonding such as:

- Graphite is a covalent network of carbon atoms that does conduct electricity due to the fact that it has delocalised (free to move) electrons.
- Titanium tetrachloride ($TiCl_4$) is a compound with low melting and boiling points. This is because it is a covalent molecular substance even though it contains a metal.

The 'remember' boxes show two ways of summarising this information about the properties of substances with different types of bonding. Use whichever one suits you best or even a mixture of both.

Remember

Property	Ionic lattice	Covalent network	Covalent molecular
Melting and boiling points	High	Very high	Low
State at room temperature	Solid	Solid	Liquid, gas or low melting point solid
Conduction of electricity	Only when molten or in solution	Never (except graphite)	Never (although water is a poor conductor)

Remember

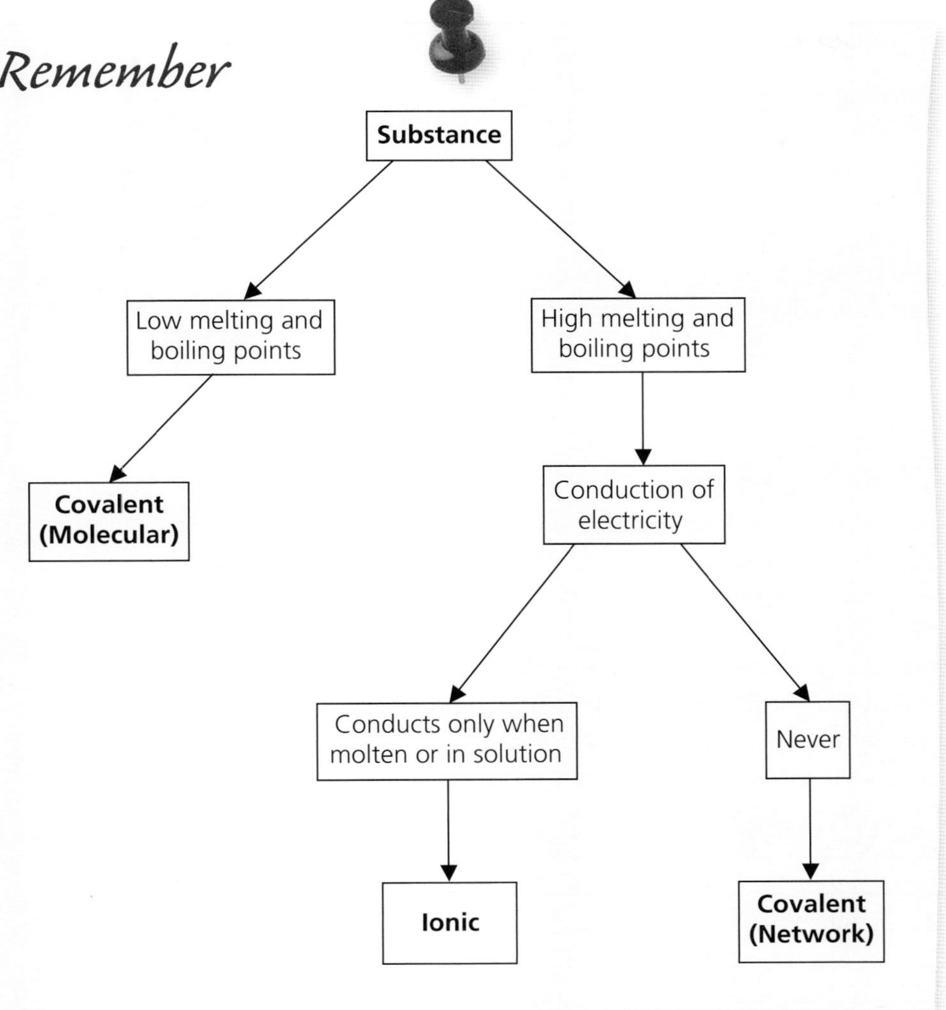

Study questions

1 Which of the following substances contains diatomic molecules?
  - **A** Calcium oxide
  - **B** Carbon dioxide
  - **C** Carbon monoxide
  - **D** Carbon tetrafluoride

2 Which of the following substances does not have a covalent network structure?
  - **A** Sulphur
  - **B** Diamond
  - **C** Silicon dioxide
  - **D** Silicon carbide

3 Which of the following has a covalent molecular structure?
  - **A** Neon
  - **B** Silicon dioxide
  - **C** Sulphur dioxide
  - **D** Sodium chloride

4 Figure 1.32 is representative of what type of structure?
   A Ionic lattice
   B Metallic bonding
   C Covalent network
   D Covalent molecule

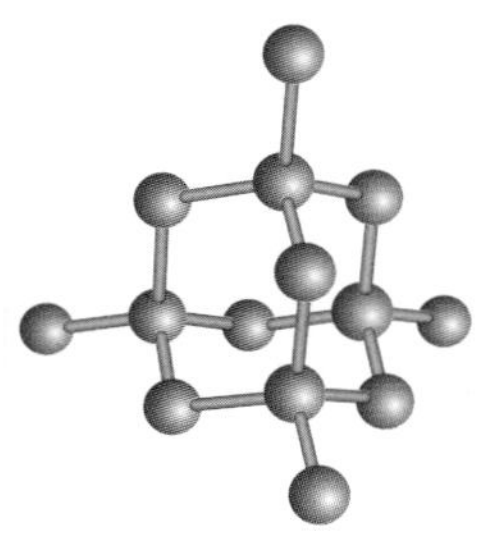

Figure 1.32

5 An unknown element is found to have a melting point of over 1000°C and a chloride of this element is also a solid at room temperature. Which of the following could be the element described?
   A Copper
   B Sulphur
   C Carbon
   D Hydrogen

6 In a molecule of ammonia all the atoms are held together by strong covalent bonds.
   a) Explain fully what a covalent bond is and how a covalent bond holds atoms together.
   b) Draw a diagram of an ammonia molecule showing all the electrons involved in holding the atoms together.
   c) Draw a diagram to show the shape of methane, ammonia and water molecules.
   d) Water has a boiling point that is higher than methane although both contain covalent bonding. Explain why water has a higher than expected boiling point.

7 The properties of four different substances are shown in the table below.

Substance	Melting point (°C)	Boiling point (°C)	Electrical conduction
A	−77	−33	No
B	1883	2503	No
C	773	1407	When molten but not when solid
D	1538	2862	Yes

Complete the table below using the letters to show the type of bonding present in each substance.

Substance	Bonding and structure
	Metallic
	Ionic
	Covalent network
	Covalent molecular

Chapter 1.5

Chemical Formulae

H_2O, CO_2, NaCl . . . where do chemists get these formulae from? In this section we will revise how to write chemical formulae.

Valency

Before we do formulae we must learn about a thing called **valency**. Valency is the number of bonds that an element can form. The valency of an element in groups 1 to 8 can be worked out using the periodic table (see Figure 1.33). This means for example that all the alkali metals have a valency of 1 and so on.

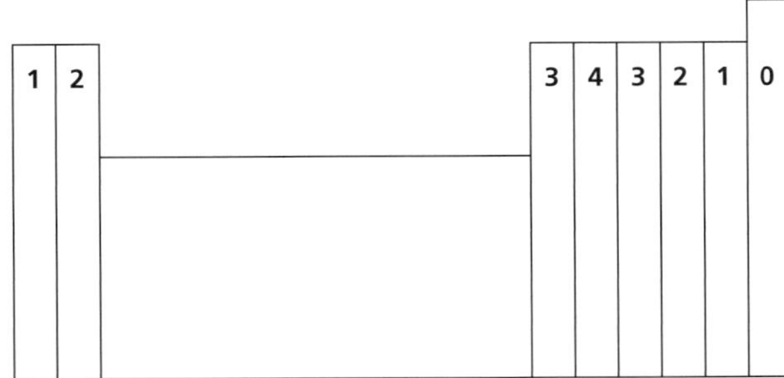

Figure 1.33 The valency of each group

Formulae

The formulae of covalent molecular compounds give the number of atoms present in the molecule, but in ionic and covalent network compounds the formulae give the simplest ratio of ions/atoms in the substance.

To write a chemical formula it is best to use the S.V.S.D.F. system shown in the examples below.

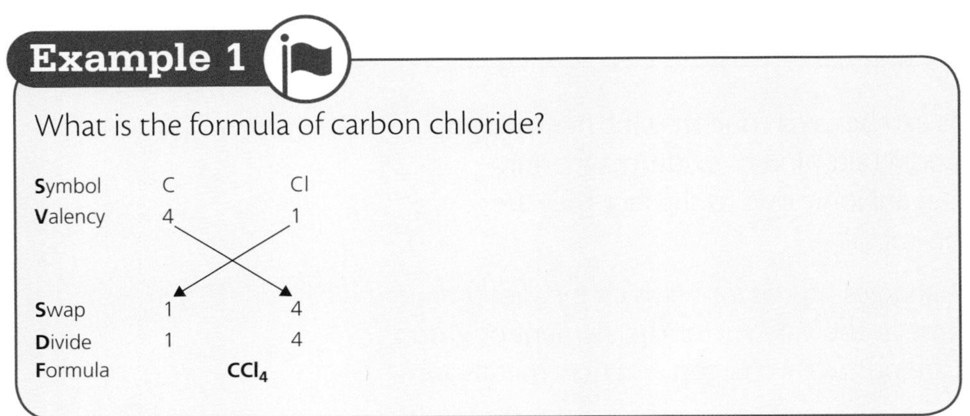

Example 1
What is the formula of carbon chloride?
Symbol C Cl
Valency 4 1
Swap 1 4
Divide 1 4
Formula CCl_4

Hints & tips

When writing formulae remember the following tips.

- ✓ *Always use your data booklet to find out the valency of an element.*
- ✓ *When dividing always use the smallest number. In the formula in example 1 the smallest number is 1 and therefore it makes no difference to the formula. If the numbers don't divide into each other (for example 2 into 3), then miss this stage out.*

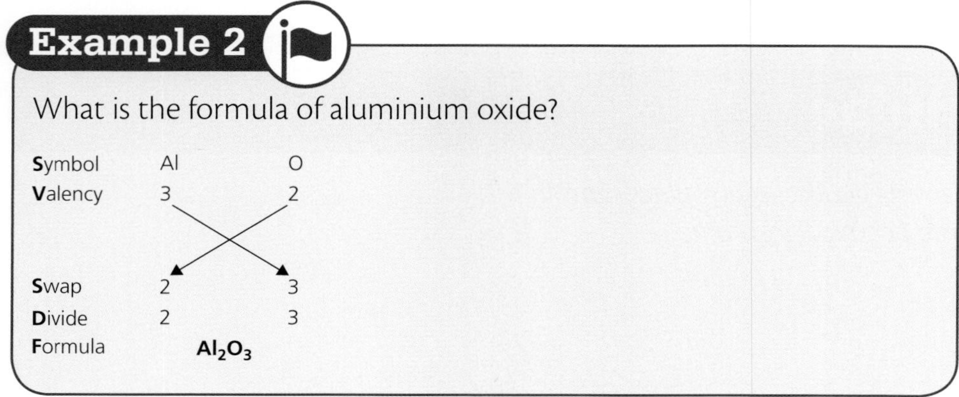

Example 2
What is the formula of aluminium oxide?
Symbol Al O
Valency 3 2
Swap 2 3
Divide 2 3
Formula Al2O3

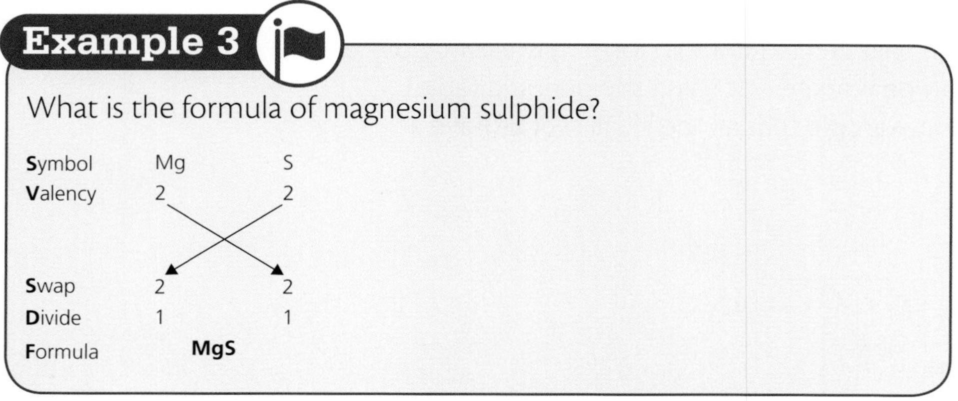

Example 3
What is the formula of magnesium sulphide?
Symbol Mg S
Valency 2 2
Swap 2 2
Divide 1 1
Formula MgS

More complex formulae involving group ions can also be produced using this same system. (The valency of group ions can be found in your data booklet along with their formulae.)

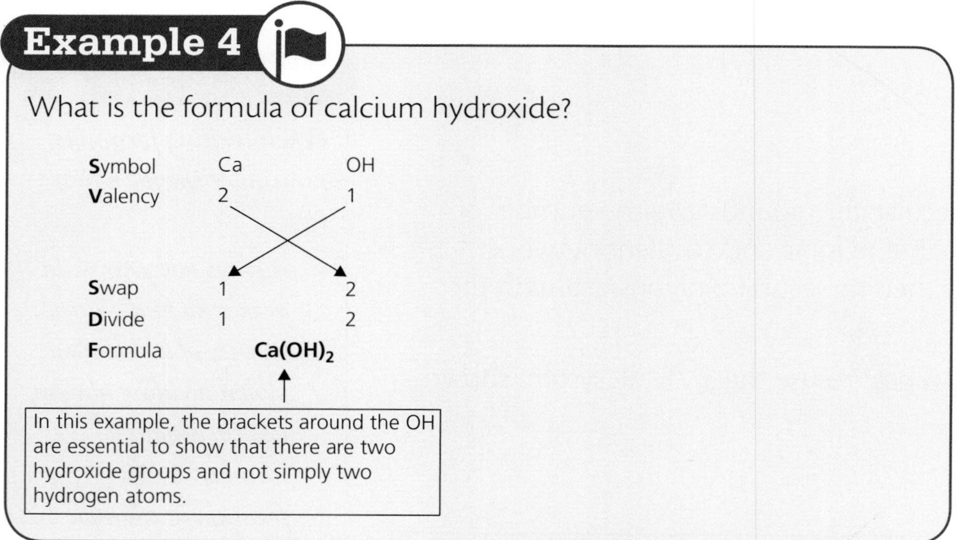

Example 4
What is the formula of calcium hydroxide?
Symbol Ca OH
Valency 2 1
Swap 1 2
Divide 1 2
Formula Ca(OH)2
In this example, the brackets around the OH are essential to show that there are two hydroxide groups and not simply two hydrogen atoms.

Formulae for ionic compounds can be taken one step further to form ionic formulae. Examples 2, 3 and 4 (aluminium oxide, magnesium sulphide and calcium hydroxide) are ionic due to the fact they are composed of a metal and a non-metal.

The ionic formula includes the charges on the ions (which is easier than it sounds!) the charges are the same as the valency for the element or group ion. Remember that all metals are positively charged and non-metals are negatively charged.

Example 5

What is the ionic formula of aluminium oxide?

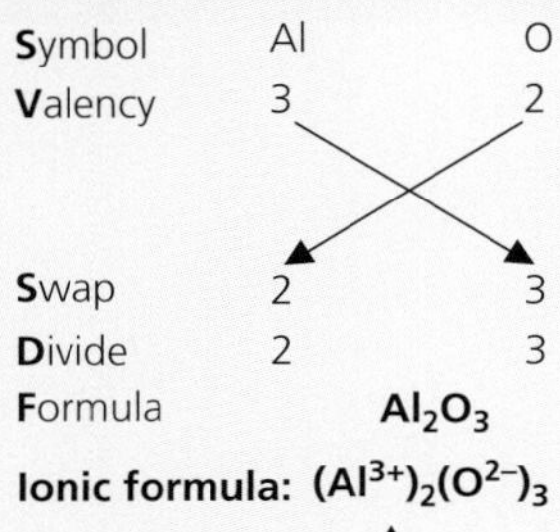

Aluminium (metal) valency = 3, charge = 3+
Oxygen (non-metal) valency = 2, charge = 2–

The ionic formula of magnesium sulphide is $Mg^{2+}S^{2-}$ and calcium hydroxide is $Ca^{2+}(OH^-)_2$.

Study questions

Go to page 29, where you will find questions on chemical formulae.

Chapter 1.6
The Mole

When you think of a mole you think of a small furry animal that lives under the ground. Not any more, because in chemistry one mole is equal to the gram formula mass of a substance. In this section we will revise mole calculations, including how to balance equations.

Calculating mass

The **gram formula mass** of a substance is the mass of one **mole** of that substance.

The relative atomic masses of selected elements are listed in your data booklet. These can be used to calculate the gram formula mass of a substance.

Example 1 

What is the mass of one mole of potassium oxide?

To calculate this all you have to do is work out the formula of potassium oxide. Then add all the relative atomic masses together. Remember to multiply if there is more than one atom.

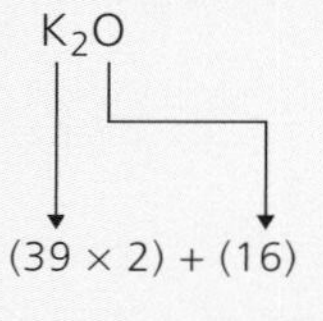

= 78 + 16 = **94 g**

So the gram formula mass of potassium oxide is 94 g.

Example 2 

What is the gram formula mass of magnesium hydroxide?

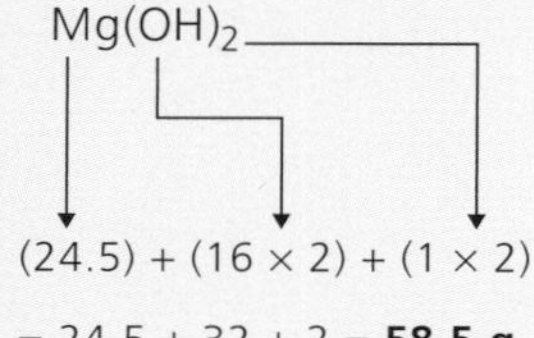

= 24.5 + 32 + 2 = **58.5 g**

Mole calculations

Mole calculations can be easily done if this simple equation triangle is remembered.

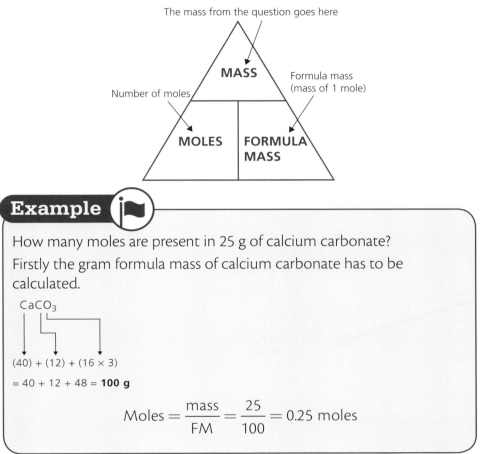

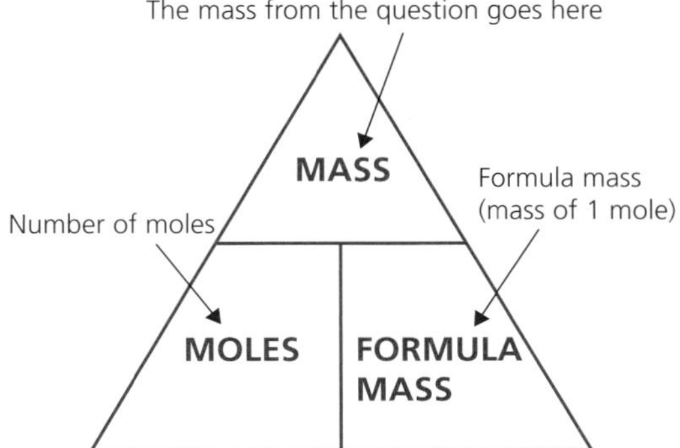

Example

How many moles are present in 25 g of calcium carbonate?

Firstly the gram formula mass of calcium carbonate has to be calculated.

$CaCO_3$

(40) + (12) + (16 × 3)

= 40 + 12 + 48 = **100 g**

$$\text{Moles} = \frac{\text{mass}}{\text{FM}} = \frac{25}{100} = 0.25 \text{ moles}$$

More calculations involving moles

Moles are also used to calculate concentrations of solutions. To do these calculations another equation triangle has to be learned.

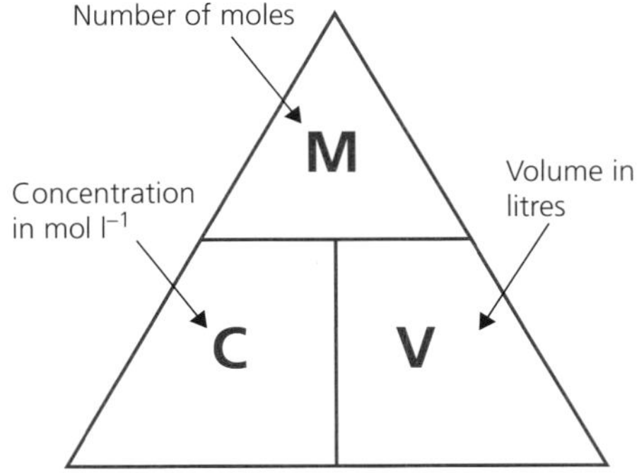

The volume used must be in litres. To convert cm^3 to litres divide by 1000. For example, if the volume is given as 250 cm^3 then in litres this is 0.25 l $\left(\frac{250}{1000} = 0.25 \text{ l}\right)$.

Example

Calculate the concentration of a sodium hydroxide solution if 2 moles are dissolved in water to give 500 cm^3 of solution.

$M = 2 \textit{ moles}$

$V = 500 \textit{ cm}^3 = 0.5 \textit{ l}$

$C = \frac{M}{V} = \frac{2}{0.5} = 4 \text{ mol l}^{-1}$

The calculations we have just looked at are commonly combined to produce one, more complicated, calculation. This allows us to use both triangles in one calculation.

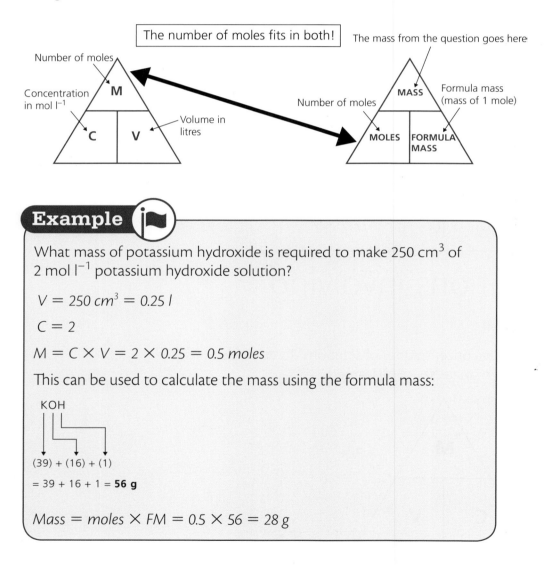

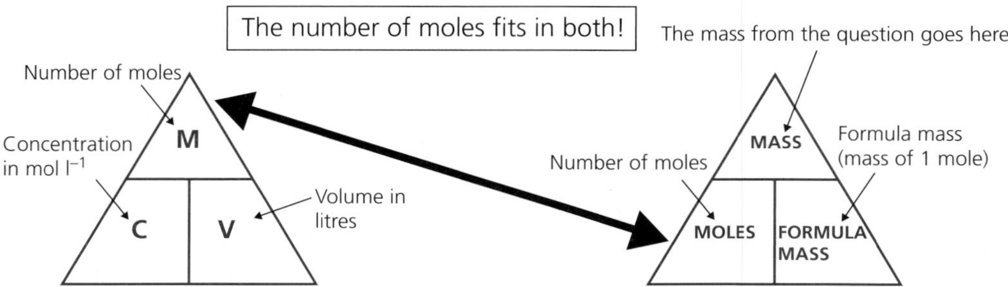

Example

What mass of potassium hydroxide is required to make 250 cm^3 of 2 mol l^{-1} potassium hydroxide solution?

$V = 250 \textit{ cm}^3 = 0.25 \textit{ l}$

$C = 2$

$M = C \times V = 2 \times 0.25 = 0.5 \textit{ moles}$

This can be used to calculate the mass using the formula mass:

KOH

(39) + (16) + (1)

= 39 + 16 + 1 = **56 g**

$\textit{Mass} = \textit{moles} \times \textit{FM} = 0.5 \times 56 = 28 \textit{ g}$

Balancing equations

A chemical reaction is said to be balanced when there are equal amounts of each element on either side of the equation.

The equation shown below is not balanced because there are two atoms of oxygen on the left and only one on the right. Atoms cannot magically appear or disappear so we must balance the equation.

$$Ca + O_2 \rightarrow CaO$$

To balance this equation we must follow several steps.

1 Check that all the formulae are correct.
2 Deal with only one element at a time. For example, there is only one calcium atom on the left and only one on the right, therefore the calcium atoms are balanced.
3 If balancing is required, put the number in front of the substance. For example, there are two oxygen atoms on the left and only one on the right, therefore multiply the compound on the right by two:

$$Ca + O_2 \rightarrow 2CaO$$

4 Check each element again and repeat step three if required. For example, there are now two calciums on the right and only one on the left, therefore multiply the calcium on the left by two:

$$2Ca + O_2 \rightarrow 2CaO$$

The equation is now balanced!

Hints & tips

Calculations involving moles and balancing equations can seem very difficult but practise as many as you can and they will become a lot easier.

Study questions

1 a) What is the correct formula of the compounds listed below?
  i. Magnesium oxide
  ii. Calcium chloride
  iii. Aluminium sulphide
  iv. Sodium fluoride
  v. Calcium nitrate
  vi. Ammonium sulphate
 b) Write the ionic formula of each of the compounds.
 c) Calculate the gram formula mass of each of the compounds.
2 Balance each of the following equations.
 a) $Mg + O_2 \rightarrow MgO$
 b) $CH_4 + O_2 \rightarrow CO_2 + H_2O$
 c) $Na + O_2 \rightarrow Na_2O$
 d) $Li + H_2O \rightarrow LiOH + H_2$
 e) $Fe + O_2 \rightarrow Fe_2O_3$
 f) $N_2 + H_2 \rightarrow NH_3$
3 Michael has been asked to prepare 250 cm^3 of 2 mol l^{-1} sodium hydroxide solution. What mass of sodium hydroxide does Michael require to produce this solution?
4 Potassium nitrate can be used as fertiliser. To test its effectiveness a farmer decides to use a 1 mol l^{-1} solution on his test crops. What mass of potassium nitrate is required to produce 1.5 litres of a solution of this concentration?

Chapter 1.7
Acids and Bases

The pH scale gives us an indication of how acidic or alkaline a substance is. In this section we will reveal what makes a substance acidic or alkaline and what happens when we add an acid and an alkali together.

The pH scale

Before we progress through this section it is important to have a look at the **pH** scale.

The pH scale is a measure of the concentration of hydrogen ions (**p**otential **H**ydrogen) and it is a continuous scale from below 0 to above 14. (We will look at hydrogen ions later in this section.)

- A pH of BELOW 7 indicates an acidic solution. (The pH paper or universal indicator solution turns a red or orange colour.)
- A pH of ABOVE 7 indicates an alkaline solution. (The pH paper or universal indicator solution turns a blue or purple colour.)
- A pH of 7 is a neutral solution such as pure water. (The pH paper or universal indicator solution will turn green.)

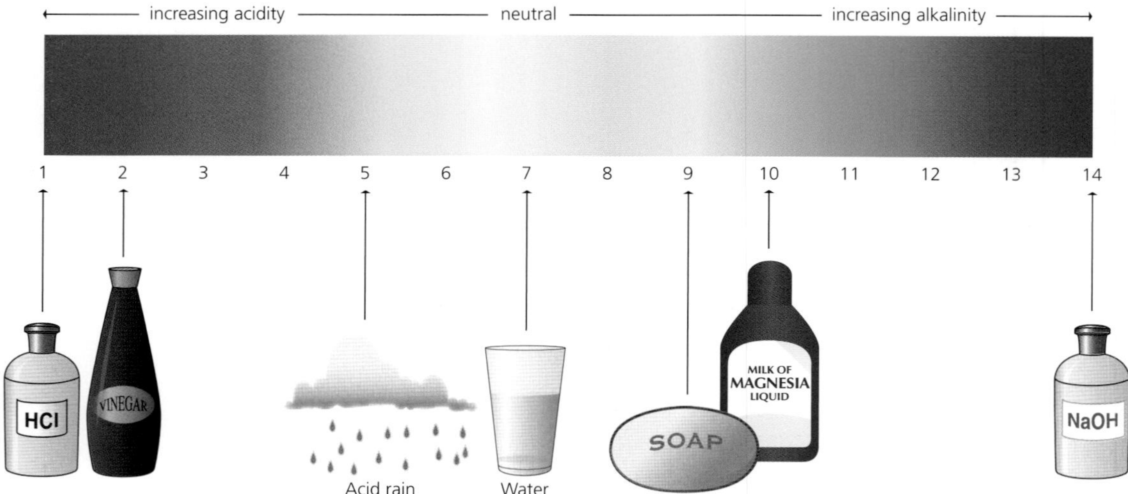

Figure 1.34 The pH scale

Acidic solutions

Acidic solutions have a pH of between 1 and 6. This is because they contain H^+ ions in a greater concentration than OH^- ions.

Hydroxide (OH^-) ions are the opposite of H^+ ions and cancel them out (see **neutralisation**). So for a solution to be acidic it must have a higher concentration of H^+ ions than OH^- ions.

H^+ ions are why acids react like they do and all acidic solutions contain H^+. All acids contain ions and as a result they conduct electricity, because the ions are free to carry the charge.

Remember

Shown below are the formulae of some common acids.

Acid name	Formula	Ionic formula
Hydrochloric acid	HCl	$H^+(aq)\ Cl^-(aq)$
Sulphuric acid	H_2SO_4	$(H^+)_2(aq)\ SO_4^{2-}(aq)$
Nitric acid	HNO_3	$H^+(aq)\ NO_3^-(aq)$
Ethanoic acid	CH_3COOH	$H^+(aq)\ CH_3COO^-(aq)$

Note that the H^+ ions are present in the ionic formula of all acids.

When an acid is diluted with water the concentration of H^+ ions is decreased. This increases the pH of the solution toward 7 because the acid is becoming less acidic.

Alkaline solutions

Alkaline solutions have a pH of between 8 and 14. This is because they contain OH^- ions. The presence of OH^- ions is the reason why alkalis react like they do and all alkaline solutions contain OH^-. Like acids, alkalis conduct electricity because they have ions that are free to carry the charge.

Remember

Listed below are the formulae of some common alkalis.

Alkali name	Formula	Ionic formula
Sodium hydroxide	$NaOH$	$Na^+(aq)\ OH^-(aq)$
Calcium hydroxide	$Ca(OH)_2$	$Ca^{2+}(aq)\ (OH^-)_2(aq)$
Lithium hydroxide	$LiOH$	$Li^+(aq)\ OH^-(aq)$

When an **alkali** is diluted with water the concentration of OH^- ions is decreased. This decreases the pH of the solution toward 7 because the alkali is becoming less alkaline.

Making acids and alkalis

Acids and alkalis can be formed by dissolving different oxides in water.

When a non-metal oxide is dissolved in water an acidic solution is produced. If a soluble metal oxide, known as a **base**, is dissolved in water, an alkaline solution is produced.

Metal oxides such as Li_2O, Na_2O and K_2O dissolve in water to produce alkaline solutions (solutions with a pH greater than 7). Notice that all the oxides of group 1 (and some of group 2) are soluble; most other metal oxides are insoluble.

Key points

- Soluble non-metal oxides produce acids.
- Soluble metal oxides (bases) produce alkalis.

Neutral solutions

Neutral solutions such as water have equal concentrations of OH^- and H^+ ions which cancel each other out. It is because of this small amount of ions that water can conduct electricity.

$$H^+ + OH^- \rightleftharpoons H_2O$$

Neutralisation

Neutralisation is the reaction of an acid with a base such as an alkali, metal oxide, metal hydroxide or carbonate. This moves the pH of the acid upwards toward 7 and the pH of the alkali downwards toward 7. All neutralisation reactions produce water.

Neutralisation occurs every day, for example in the treatment of acid indigestion or adding lime to lakes to reduce their acidity and counteract the effects of acid rain.

There are two main equations for neutralisation.

acid + alkali → salt + water
acid + base → salt + water

The name of the **salt** produced is dependent on the acid and alkali that reacted. Naming the salt is straightforward if you learn the table in the 'remember' box.

Remember

Acid name	Salt name ends in
Hydrochloric acid	chloride
Sulphuric acid	sulphate
Nitric acid	nitrate

Example

hydrochloric acid + sodium hydroxide → sodium chloride + water

The salt is produced when the hydrogen ion of the acid is replaced by the metal ion of the alkali. See page 33 for why water is produced.

During neutralisation the H^+ ion from the acid joins with the OH^- ion from the alkali. This is why water is formed in these reactions:

$$H^+ + OH^- \rightarrow H_2O.$$

This can be illustrated clearly using ionic equations.

Ionic equations

Previously you learned the ionic formulae of acids and alkalis. These can now be used to form ionic equations.

A **spectator ion** is like a spectator at a football match. They are there at the game but are not taking part in the game. They are simply spectators watching the reaction taking place.

Example 1

hydrochloric acid + sodium hydroxide → sodium chloride + water

$$HCl + NaOH \rightarrow NaCl + H_2O$$

The ionic equation simply combines their ionic formulae.

$$H^+(aq)\ Cl^-(aq) + Na^+(aq) + OH^-(aq) \rightarrow Na^+(aq)\ Cl^-(aq) + H_2O(l)$$

This can be shortened further by removing the spectator ions.

$$H^+(aq)\ \cancel{Cl^-}(aq) + \cancel{Na^+}(aq) + OH^-(aq) \rightarrow \cancel{Na^+}(aq)\ \cancel{Cl^-}(aq) + H_2O(l)$$

When the spectator ions are removed we are left with a very familiar equation.

$$H^+ + OH^- \rightarrow H_2O$$

Key points

The spectator ions are ions that are present during the reaction, but are unchanged by the reaction.

Acids can also react with other bases such as metal carbonates. When an acid reacts with any carbonate, carbon dioxide is produced.

Example 2

$$2HCl + CaCO_3 \rightarrow CaCl_2 + H_2O + CO_2$$

The same method as before is used to name the salt and we can also write an ionic equation for this reaction:

$$2H^+(aq) + 2Cl^-(aq) + Ca^{2+}(aq) + CO_3^{2-}(aq) \rightarrow Ca^{2+}(aq) + 2Cl^-(aq) + H_2O(l) + CO_2(g)$$

(Note that CO_2 and H_2O are covalent so they can't have an ionic formula!)

When the spectator ions are removed from this equation we are left with:

$$2H^+(aq) + CO_3^{2-}(aq) \rightarrow H_2O(l) + CO_2(g)$$

Titrations

An acid-base **titration** is a procedure which is used to determine the concentration of an acid. An accurately measured volume of a base of known concentration is reacted with an acid until the acid is neutralised. An indicator is usually added to provide a colour change at the point when neutralisation is complete.

There are several ways to go about calculating the concentrations from titrations but this is by far the easiest method.

$$PVC_{(acid)} = PVC_{(alkali)}$$

P = The number of 'Hs' the acid or alkali has.

V = The volume in litres

C = The concentration in mol l^{-1}

Example

What concentration is a sulphuric acid solution if 500 cm^3 is neutralised by 500 cm^3 of 4 mol l^{-1} sodium hydroxide?

$P = 2\ (H_2SO_4)$

$V = 500\ cm^3 = 0.5\ l$

$C = ????$

$$PVC_{(acid)} = PVC_{(alkali)}$$
$$2 \times 0.5 \times C = 1 \times 0.5 \times 4$$
$$1 \times C = 2$$
$$C = \frac{2}{1}$$
$$C = 2\ mol\ l^{-1}$$

$P = 1\ (NaOH)$

$V = 500\ cm^3 = 0.5\ l$

$C = 4\ mol\ l^{-1}$

Study questions

1 0.75 mol of citric acid was dissolved in 250 cm^3 of water. What was the concentration of the solution formed?

A 0.003 mol l^{-1}

B 0.3 mol l^{-1}

C 3 mol l^{-1}

D 333 mol l^{-1}

2 Which of the following compounds is classed as a salt?

A Sodium choride

B Calcium oxide

C Sulphur dioxide

D Hydrogen chloride

3 Which of the following oxides dissolves in water to produce an acidic solution?

A SiO_2
B SO_2
C Fe_2O_3
D PbO_2

4 An unknown white solid is soluble in water. The unknown solid also reacts with hydrochloric acid to produce carbon dioxide gas. The solid could be:

A sodium oxide
B aluminium oxide
C copper(II) carbonate
D potassium carbonate

5 The spectator ions in the following equation are:

$$H^+(aq) + NO_3^-(aq) + K^+(aq) + OH^-(aq) \rightarrow K^+(aq) + NO_3^-(aq) + H_2O\ (l)$$

A H^+ and K^+
B H^+ and OH^-
C K^+ and NO_3^-
D K^+ and OH^-

6 Which of the following oxides, when shaken with water, would leave the pH unchanged?

A Carbon dioxide
B Copper oxide
C Sodium oxide
D Sulphur dioxide

7 A technician is making a solution of sodium hydroxide by dissolving solid sodium oxide in water to produce a concentrated solution of sodium hydroxide.

a) Write the word equation for this reaction.
b) Rewrite the equation using chemical formulae.
c) Suggest a pH for the solution produced.
d) Suggest why using this method to try to produce a solution of aluminium hydroxide would be difficult.

8 The concentration of ethanoic acid in vinegar can be determined by titration using a sample of 0.5 mol l^{-1} sodium hydroxide solution with 10 cm^3 of the acid.

The following results were recorded.

Titration	Volume of sodium hydroxide (cm^3)
1	21.3
2	20.1
3	19.9

Calculate the concentration in mol l^{-1} of the ethanoic acid in the vinegar.

Unit 2 Nature's Chemistry

Chapter 2.1
Homologous Series

You will have already revised that hydrocarbons are compounds made up of carbon and hydrogen only. In this section we will revise families of hydrocarbons. These families are known as homologous series.

Key points 

A homologous series is a family of compounds with similar chemical properties that can be represented by a general formula.

A good way to explain what is meant by a **homologous series** is to look at a human family. John McBride is the oldest member of the McBride family and he has one sister called Grace McBride and one brother called Ethan McBride. They all belong to the same family – that is why they have the same ending to their name. Although they are all in the same family they look slightly different and act in slightly different ways.

The McBride family – a homologous series

This is similar to any homologous series. The compounds in a homologous series all have the same ending to their name and have similar properties but each member is slightly different. The simplest homologous series is called the **alkanes**.

Alkanes

All alkanes have the same ending to their names: –ANE (for example, methane). The alkanes are very important **hydrocarbons** because of their many uses, such as those shown in the pictures.

Figure 2.1 Alkanes include methane which is used for cooking and heating and octane which is used as petrol for cars

Listed below are the name, molecular formula and structural formula of the first four members of the alkane homologous series. The names, molecular formulae and structural formulae of the first *eight* alkanes must be learned.

Name	Molecular formula	Full structural formula
methane	CH_4	H | H—C—H | H
ethane	C_2H_6	H H | | H—C—C—H | | H H
propane	C_3H_8	H H H | | | H—C—C—C—H | | | H H H
butane	C_4H_{10}	H H H H | | | | H—C—C—C—C—H | | | | H H H H

Hints & tips

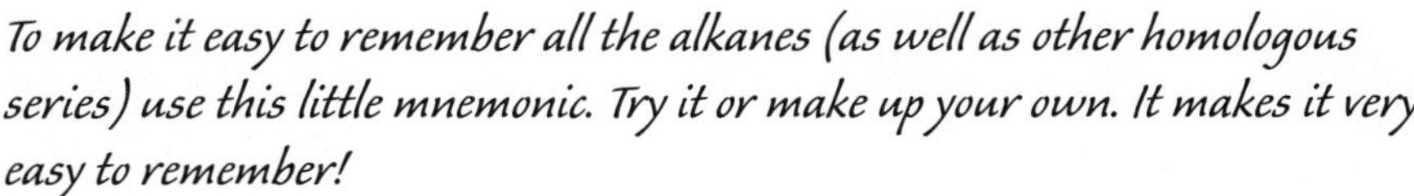

To make it easy to remember all the alkanes (as well as other homologous series) use this little mnemonic. Try it or make up your own. It makes it very easy to remember!

Monkeys	*Methane*	CH_4
Eat	*Ethane*	C_2H_6
Peanut	*Propane*	C_3H_8
Butter	*Butane*	C_4H_{10}
Perhaps	*Pentane*	C_5H_{12}
Harry	*Hexane*	C_6H_{14}
Heptane	*Heptane*	C_7H_{16}
Objects	*Octane*	C_8H_{18}

All homologous series have what is known as a general formula. The general formula allows you to work out the molecular formula of any alkane.

The general formula of the alkanes is $\mathbf{C_nH_{2n+2}}$. (Where *n* is the number of carbon atoms.)

Example

What is the molecular formula of pentane?

Using the mnemonic you can work out that pentane is the fifth alkane and therefore has 5 carbon atoms (n = 5). To calculate the number of hydrogen atoms use the formula:

$$C_nH_{2n+2} = C_5H_{2\times 5+2}$$

So the molecular formula of pentane is $\mathbf{C_5H_{12}}$.

As with all homologous series, there is a regular change in chemical and physical properties of alkanes. For example, the boiling point of the alkanes increases but the flammability decreases as the carbon chain length increases.

Alkenes

The second homologous series is the **alkenes**. All alkenes have the same ending to their name: –ENE (for example, ethene). They are different from the alkanes because they contain a carbon to carbon double bond.

The names, molecular formulae and structural formulae of the first three alkenes are in the table below. (Note that there is no methene because there must be at least two carbon atoms to form a double carbon to carbon bond.)

Name	Molecular formula	Full structural formula
ethene	C_2H_4	H H \ / C=C / \ H H
propene	C_3H_6	H H H | | / H—C—C=C | \ H H
butene	C_4H_8	H H H H | | | / H—C—C—C=C | | \ H H H

The alkenes have the general formula: $\boldsymbol{C_nH_{2n}}$.

Cycloalkanes

The third homologous series is the **cycloalkanes**. All cycloalkanes have the ending –ANE but start with CYCLO- (for example, cyclopropane).

The names, molecular formulae and structural formulae of the first two cycloalkanes are in the table below.

Name	Molecular formula	Full structural formula
cyclopropane	C_3H_6	H H \ / C / \ H—C—C—H / \ H H
cyclobutane	C_4H_8	H H | | H—C—C—H | | H—C—C—H | | H H

The cycloalkanes have the same general formula as the alkenes: $\boldsymbol{C_nH_{2n}}$.

Saturated or unsaturated?

The alkenes are described as **unsaturated hydrocarbons**. This means that they have a carbon to carbon double bond. This makes them more reactive than the alkanes, which only have single bonds. The alkanes are said to be **saturated hydrocarbons** because they only contain single carbon to carbon bonds. Although cycloalkanes have the same general formula as the alkenes, they are saturated like alkanes because they only have single bonds.

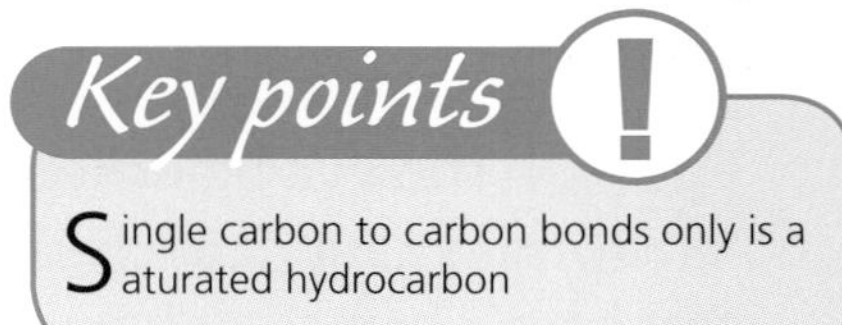

Key points
Single carbon to carbon bonds only is a Saturated hydrocarbon

Addition reactions

Alkenes, because they are unsaturated, are more reactive than alkanes and cycloalkanes. The double bond allows them to take part in **addition reactions** which involve the addition of a molecule, such as water, or a diatomic molecule, such as hydrogen, across the double bond.

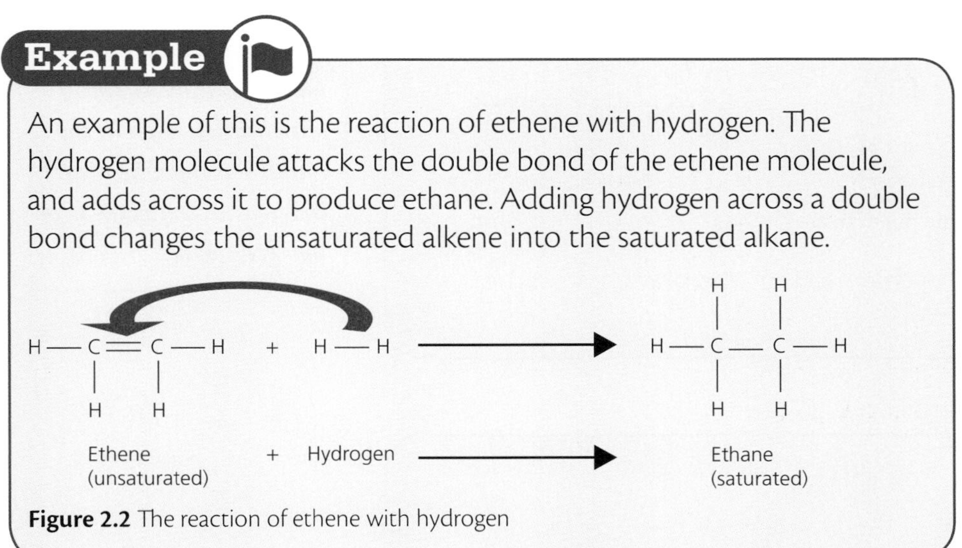

Example

An example of this is the reaction of ethene with hydrogen. The hydrogen molecule attacks the double bond of the ethene molecule, and adds across it to produce ethane. Adding hydrogen across a double bond changes the unsaturated alkene into the saturated alkane.

Figure 2.2 The reaction of ethene with hydrogen

Alkenes can be identified because they have this capability for addition reactions. When bromine, which is brown in colour, is added to an alkene it is immediately decolourised. This doesn't happen with a saturated hydrocarbon like the alkanes or cycloalkanes because they don't have a double bond for the bromine to add across. If a carbon to carbon double bond is present when bromine is added to the solution, the brown colour of the bromine will quickly disappear.

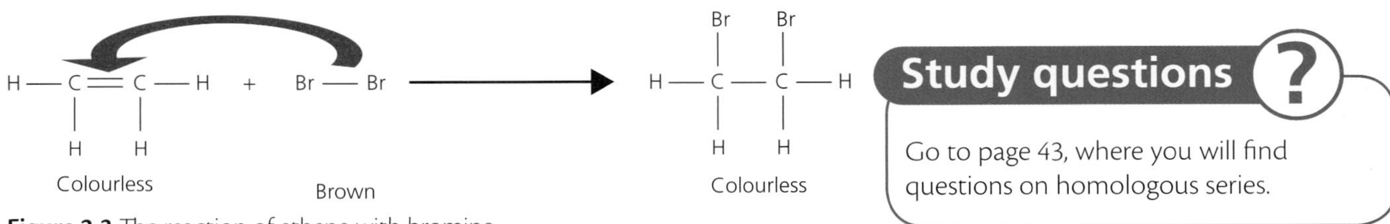

Figure 2.3 The reaction of ethene with bromine

Study questions

Go to page 43, where you will find questions on homologous series.

Chapter 2.2
Branched Hydrocarbons

Figure 2.4 shows a branched chain hydrocarbon with the name 3-methylpentane. Branched chain hydrocarbons are simply hydrocarbons that have a branch or branches coming off the chain.

Branched hydrocarbons do look difficult to name and their names seem to be very complicated, but the rules are simple.

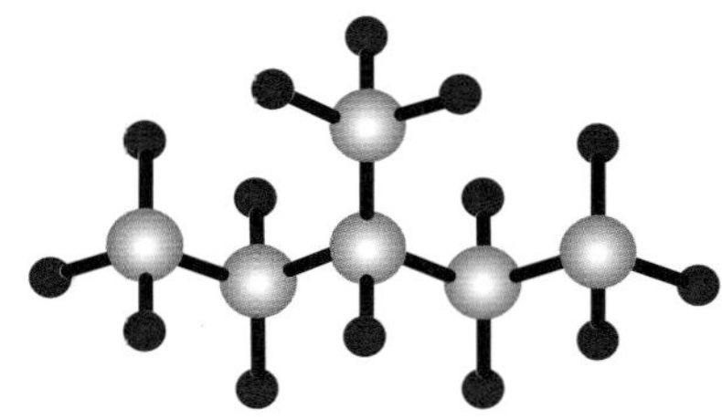

Figure 2.4 3-methylpentane

Hints & tips

Practise naming and drawing as many branched hydrocarbons as you can. The more you practise the easier it will become. Note the punctuation used in the name – it must be written this way in the exam to be marked correct.

What you should know

The rules

1. Find the *longest* carbon chain and name as normal (for example 5 carbon atoms means it is pentane).
2. Identify the branch and name from Figure 2.5 (R in the diagram is any carbon chain, i.e. the longest chain).

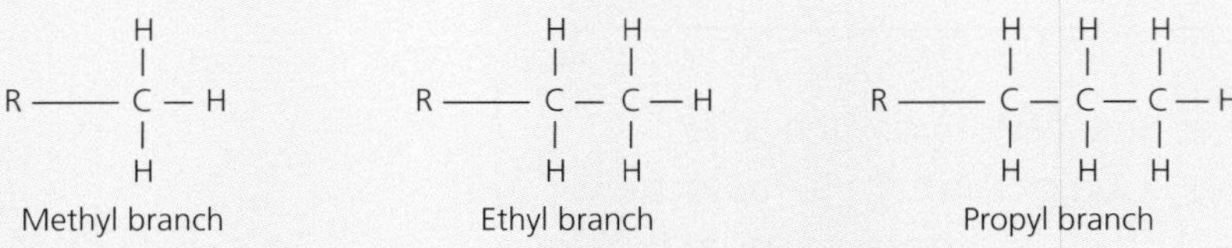

Figure 2.5 Three examples of branches of hydrocarbons

3. Number the carbons in the chain so that the branch is on the lowest possible number.

Example 1

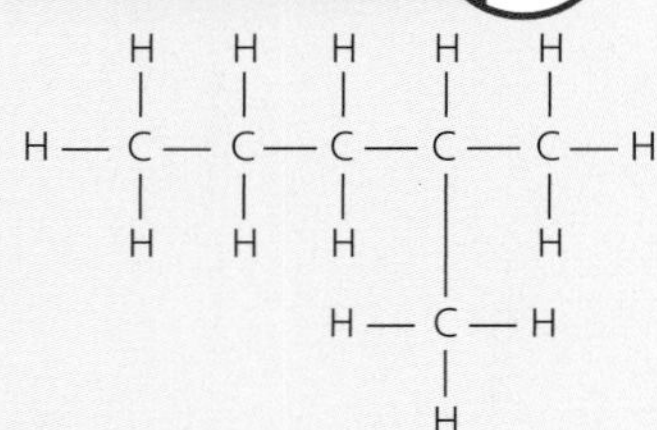

Figure 2.6 What is the name of this branched hydrocarbon?

Shortened structural formula: $CH_3CH_2CH_2CH(CH_3)CH_3$

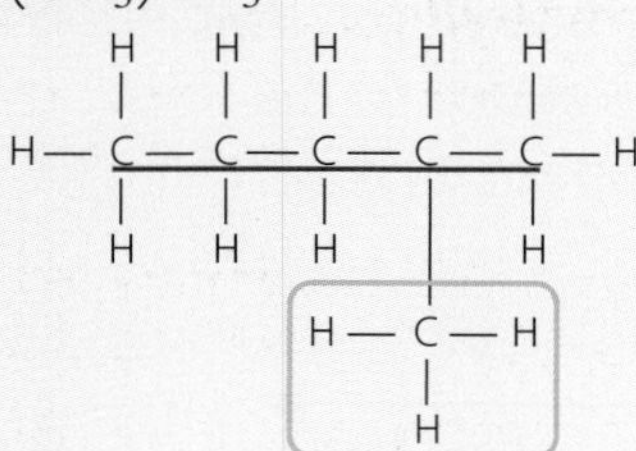

1. The longest chain has five carbons (shown by the red line).
2. The branch has one carbon (shown by the green box).
3. The branch is on carbon 2 not 4 (because you always use the lowest number).

So the name is **2-methylpentane**.

There can be more than one branch. If more than one branch is present, then a prefix must be used:

- di- (2 branches)
- tri- (3 branches)
- tetra- (4 branches).

Branches are named in alphabetical order so ethyl will always come before methyl.

Example 2

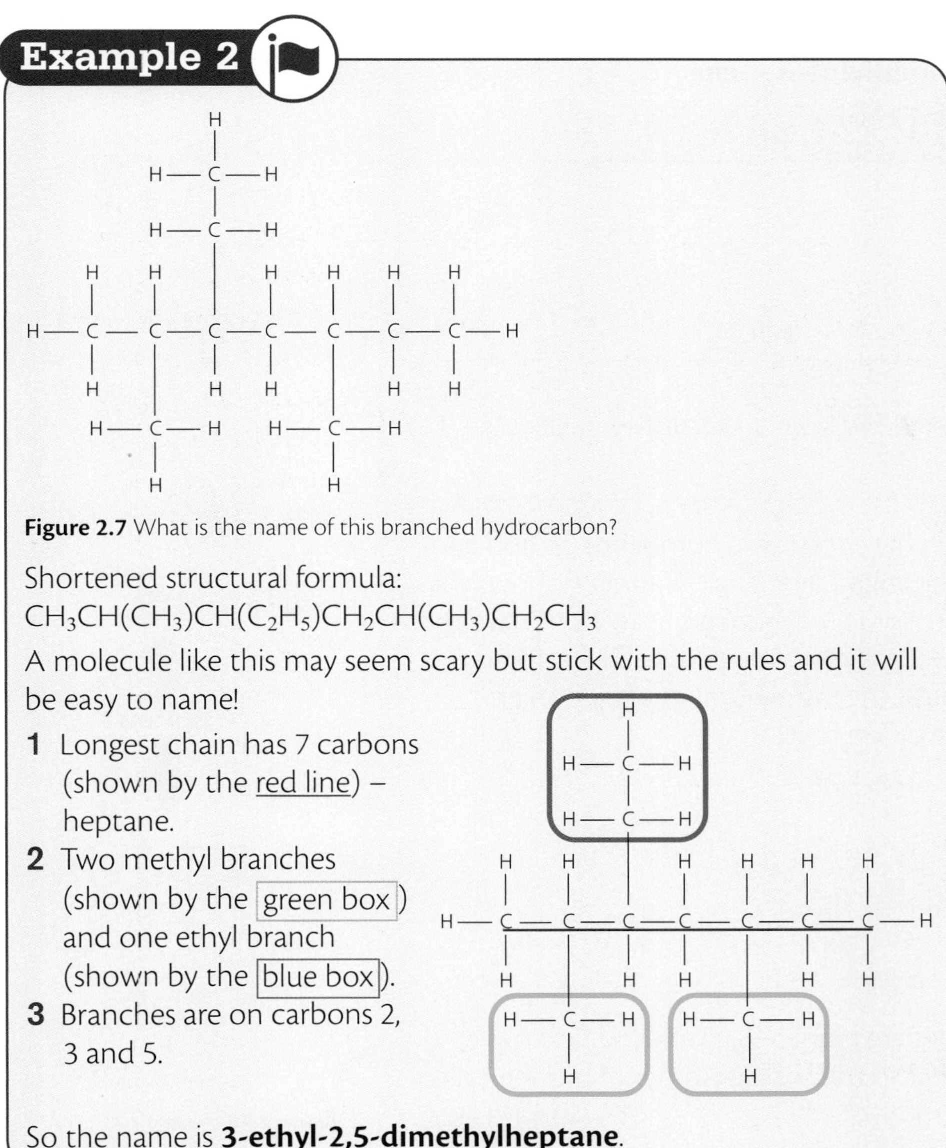

Figure 2.7 What is the name of this branched hydrocarbon?

Shortened structural formula:
$CH_3CH(CH_3)CH(C_2H_5)CH_2CH(CH_3)CH_2CH_3$

A molecule like this may seem scary but stick with the rules and it will be easy to name!

1. Longest chain has 7 carbons (shown by the red line) – heptane.
2. Two methyl branches (shown by the green box) and one ethyl branch (shown by the blue box).
3. Branches are on carbons 2, 3 and 5.

So the name is **3-ethyl-2,5-dimethylheptane**.

The same rules apply when naming alkenes with one difference: the position of the double bond must be identified. The number showing the position (again the lowest possible) is placed before the –ene.

Example 3

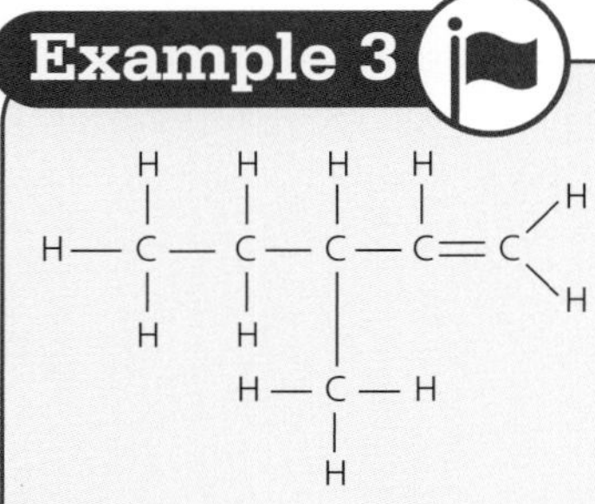

Figure 2.8 What is the name of this alkene?

The name of this alkene is **3-methylpent-1-ene**.

Shortened structural formula: $CH_3CH_2CH(CH_3)CH{=}CH_2$

Isomers

Key points

Isomers are compounds that have the same molecular formula but a different structural formula.

Isomers are compounds which have the same number of carbon and hydrogen atoms but they are arranged differently. Figure 2.9 shows the example of cyclopropane as an isomer of propene. They both have the molecular formula of C_3H_6 but the alkenes have a double bond whereas the cycloalkanes don't. Both have the same number of carbon and hydrogen atoms but they have different structures.

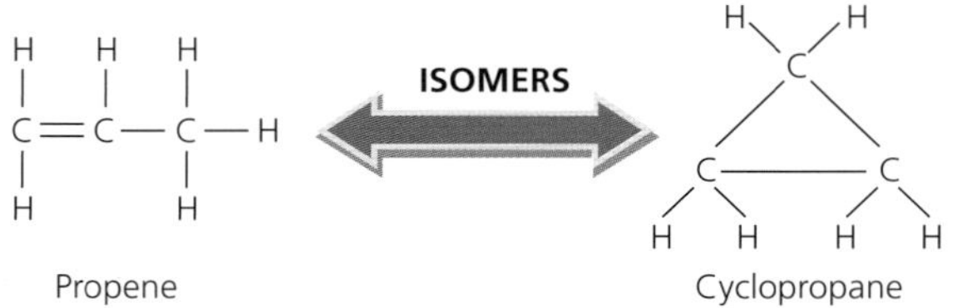

Figure 2.9 Cyclopropane is an isomer of propene

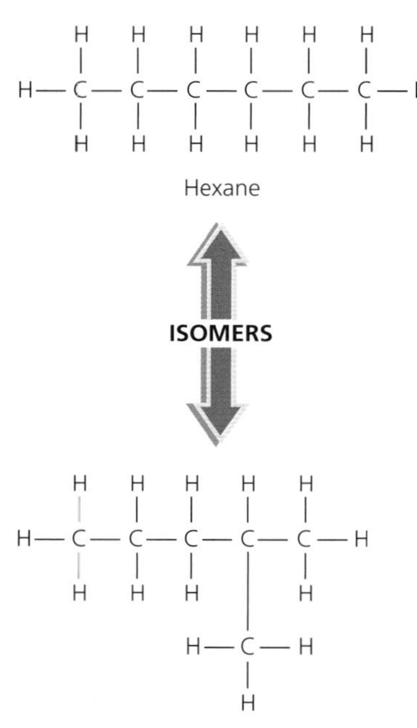

Figure 2.10 Hexane and 2-methylpentane (an isomer of hexane)

Isomers of straight chain alkanes are branched alkanes. For example, Figure 2.10 shows a molecule of hexane and an isomer of hexane called 2-methylpentane.

Isomers have different properties because they have different structures. This difference in physical properties is illustrated in the table below.

Property	Hexane	2-methylpentane
Melting point	−95 °C	−153 °C
Boiling point	69 °C	60 °C
Molecular mass	86	86

Study questions 

1 Figure 2.11 shows the structure of neopentane, which is an extremely flammable gas.

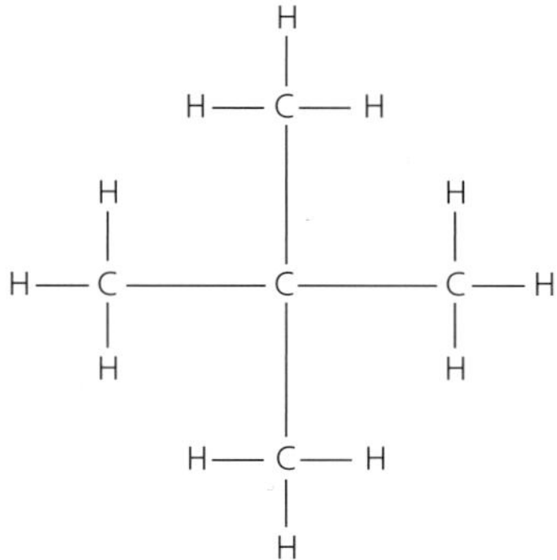

Figure 2.11

The systematic name of the compound shown in Figure 2.11 is:

A 3,2-dimethylbutane

B 2,2-dimethylpropane

C 2,3-dimethylbutane

D 3,2-dimethylpropane

2 The first three members of the alkynes homologous series is shown in Figure 2.12.

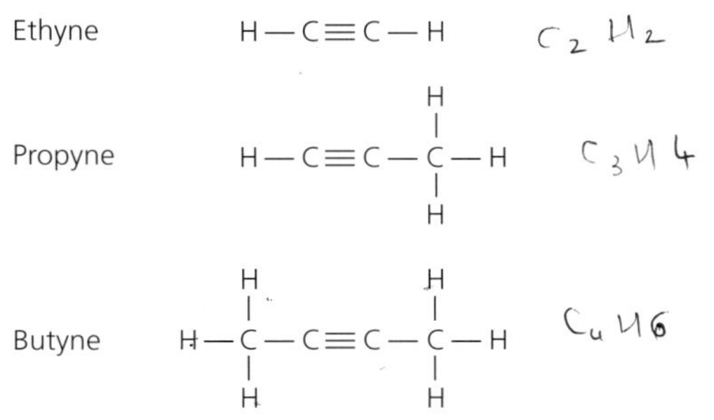

Ethyne H—C≡C—H C_2H_2

Propyne H—C≡C—CH₃ C_3H_4

Butyne H—CH₂—C≡C—CH₂—H C_4H_6

Figure 2.12

The general formula of this homologous series is:

A C_nH_{2n}

B C_nH_{2n-2}

C C_nH_{2n+2}

D C_nH_n

3 Which of the following molecules is an isomer of butane?

A Butene

B 2-methylpropane

C Cyclobutane

D 2-methylbutane

4 What is the correct systematic name for the following compound?
$CH_3CH(CH_3)CH_2CH_2CH_2CH_3$
A Heptane
B Hexane
C 2-methylhexane
D 2-methylheptane

5 What type of reaction is represented by the following equation?
$C_2H_4 \rightarrow C_2H_5OH$
A Addition
B Combustion
C Hydrolysis
D Fermentation

6 Volatile organic compounds (VOCs) are used in paints as solvents and the VOC content s displayed on most paint cans. An example of a VOC compound used in paints is methanal, which is the first member of the aldehydes homologous series. The structural formula of methanal is shown in Figure 2.13.

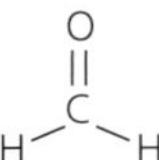

Figure 2.13

a) What is a homologous series?
b) What is the molecular formula of methanal?

7 A pupil was testing for unsaturation in four unknown organic compounds. He recorded his results in the table below.

Hydrocarbon	Molecular formula	Observations on adding bromine solution	Saturated or unsaturated?
A	C_5H_{10}		Saturated
B	C_5H_{10}		Unsaturated
C	C_5H_{12}	Remains brown	Saturated
D	C_5H_8	Brown to colourless	Unsaturated

a) Complete the table with the observations that you would expect to see with molecules A and B.
b) Draw the full structural formula of molecule B.
c) Molecules A and B have the same molecular formula but different structures. What name is given to two such molecules?

Chapter 2.3
Consumer Products

In this section we will continue to revise the various homologous series. We will specifically look at their importance in the manufacturing of consumer products.

Alcohols

When we think of alcohols, we think of alcoholic drinks such as beers and wines, but alcohols are another homologous series. They have the general formula $\mathbf{C_nH_{2n+1}OH}$.

Alkanols, or alcohols as they are commonly known, are a family of compounds with a hydroxyl **functional group** (–OH). The second member of the alcohol homologous series is ethanol. The table below shows ethanol's formulae.

<table>
<tr><td>Molecular formula</td><td>C_2H_5OH</td></tr>
<tr><td>Full structural formula</td><td>   H   H
      | |
H—C—C—OH
      | |
      H   H</td></tr>
<tr><td>Shortened structural formula</td><td>CH_3CH_2OH</td></tr>
</table>

Ethanol is the alcohol that is found in alcoholic drinks. The functional group (–OH) is the part of the molecule that dictates the properties of alcohols, in other words, the functional group makes the molecule function or react in the way it does. Think of the functional group as being the brain of the molecule, controlling the way it reacts.

As with any homologous series there are many members of the alcohol family and we use the same rules as before to name them (see Figures 2.14 and 2.15).

Hints & tips

Note that the position of the functional group does not have to be identified when naming methanol and ethanol as it can only be on the first carbon atom.

```
      H   H   H
      |   |   |
  H — C — C — C — H
      |   |   |
      H   O   H
          |
          H
```

Figure 2.14 Propan-2-ol

```
              H
              |
          H — C — H
              |
      H   H   |   H
      |   |   |   |
  H — C — C — C — C — H
      |   |   |   |
      H   H   O   H
              |
              H
```

Figure 2.15 2-methylbutan-2-ol

Alcohols are a very important family of compounds because of their many and varied uses, such as solvents in perfumes, as a replacement to the toxic metal mercury in thermometers, and as a **fuel**.

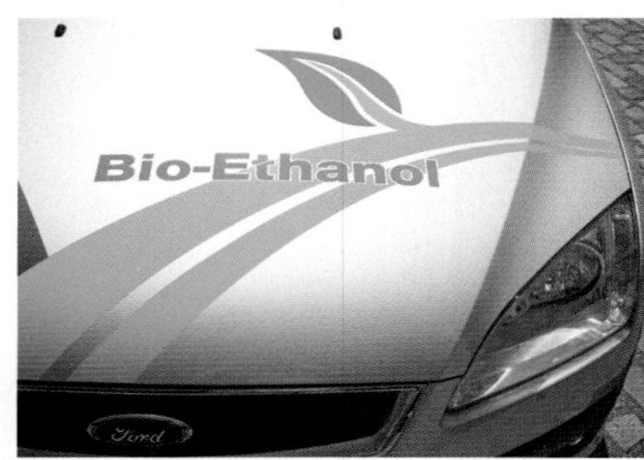

Figure 2.16 Alcohols have many uses including perfumes and fuels

Carboxylic acids (alkanoic acids)

Carboxylic acids or **alkanoic acids** are a family of compounds with the carboxyl functional group (–COOH).

```
    H   H   O
    |   |   ||
H — C — C — C
    |   |    \
    H   H     OH
```

CH_3CH_2COOH

Figure 2.17 The structural formula and shortened structural formula of propanoic acid – a member of the carboxylic acid family

When naming carboxylic acids, remember that the position of the functional group does not have to be named as it is always on the end carbon.

Carboxylic acids have various uses. They are used in the manufacture of **esters**, soap and medicines such as aspirin. Ethanoic acid is better known as vinegar!

Esters

Esters are formed by the condensation reaction known as esterification between an alcohol and a carboxylic acid. They have the functional group (–COO–) which is called the ester link.

$R^1-C(=O)-O-R^2$

Figure 2.18 The ester functional group

Esters are an important class of compounds as they can be used as solvents, and as perfumes and flavourings due to their pleasant smell and taste. For example, the ester ethyl ethanoate has a sweet smell very similar to that of pear drop sweets.

My name is Ester and I am a COO!

The production of esters is a reversible reaction, which means it goes both ways as can be seen by the double arrow in the equation below. Some of the ester produced breaks back down into the reactants.

alcohol + carboxylic acid ⇌ ester + water

Esters are produced in the lab by reacting a carboxylic acid and an alcohol in the presence of a concentrated sulphuric acid catalyst. The mixture is heated in a water bath because the reactants and products are highly flammable. The test tube is also fitted with a wet paper towel condenser to prevent the loss of any products. The cotton wool 'bung' is fitted to prevent loss of product and as a safety precaution to prevent any acid from spitting out from the test tube.

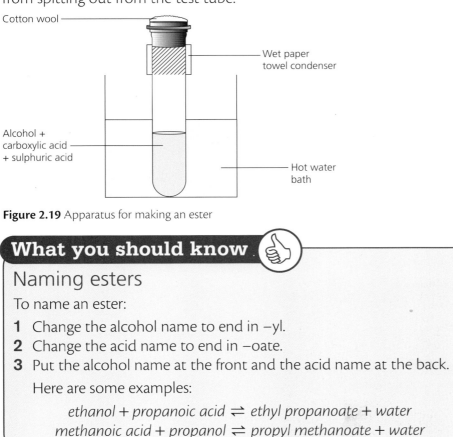

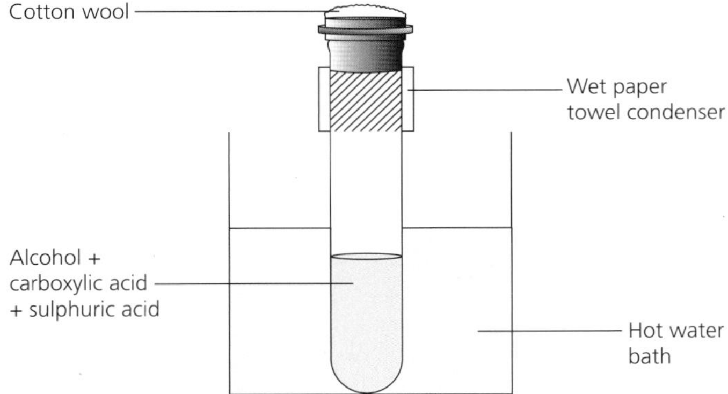

Figure 2.19 Apparatus for making an ester

What you should know

Naming esters

To name an ester:

1. Change the alcohol name to end in –yl.
2. Change the acid name to end in –oate.
3. Put the alcohol name at the front and the acid name at the back.

   Here are some examples:

ethanol + propanoic acid ⇌ ethyl propanoate + water

methanoic acid + propanol ⇌ propyl methanoate + water

Esters are formed by a condensation reaction. This means that, along with the ester, water is also produced. It is important to look at where the water comes from as this gives a clear picture of how the ester is formed and will help us in Unit 3 when looking at condensation polymerisation.

H₂O
Howdy! My name is Cowboy John. I use my lasso in condensation reactions to remove the water. I remove an H atom from the **hydroxyl group** of the alcohol and an –OH group from the acid. Feel free to join in folks – YEE-HAW!

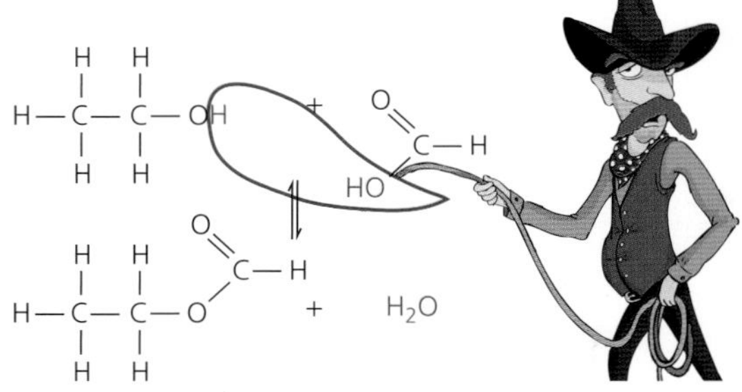

Figure 2.20 How esters are formed

The removal of water allows the oxygen of the alcohol to join with the carbon of the **carboxyl group**.

$$\textit{ethanol} + \textit{methanoic acid} \rightleftharpoons \textit{ethyl methanoate} + \textit{water}$$

This reaction can also be represented using a shortened structural formula:

$$CH_3CH_2OH + HCOOH \rightleftharpoons CH_3CH_2OOCH + H_2O$$

When naming an ester from the structural formula it is important to remember that the section of the ester that contains the C=O came from the acid. Some examples are shown in Figure 2.21:

$CH_3CH_2—C(=O)—O—CH_2—CH_3$
ethyl propanoate

$H—C(=O)—O—CH_2—CH_2—CH_3$
propyl methanoate

$CH_3CH_2CH_2—C(=O)—O—CH_3$
methyl butanoate

$CH_3—C(=O)—O—CH_2—CH_2—CH_3$
propyl ethanoate

Figure 2.21 Examples of naming esters from structural formulae

Study questions

1 What is the correct systematic name for the following compound?
$CH_3CH(OH)CH_2CH_2CH_3$

A Pentane
B Pentan-2-ol
C Pentan-3-ol
D 2-methylpentane

2 Which of the following can be classed as a carboxylic acid?

A $C_6H_{14}O$
B $C_6H_{13}OH$
C $C_6H_{13}COOH$
D $C_2H_5COOC_3H_7$

3 The name of the molecule in Figure 2.22 is:

```
     H
     |     //O     H   H   H
  H—C—C           |   |   |
     |     \O—C—C—C—H
     H            |   |   |
                  H   H   H
```

Figure 2.22

A propyl ethanoate
B ethyl propanoate
C propanoic acid
D ethanoic acid

4 During the formation of an ester which two functional groups combine during the process?

A Hydroxyl and carbonyl
B Hydroxyl and carboxyl
C Amine and carboxyl
D Carbonyl and carboxyl

5 Most sterilising pads used in hospitals contain a 65% solution of isopropyl alcohol in water. Isopropyl alcohol has the systematic name propan-2-ol.

a) Draw the full structural formula of isopropyl alcohol.

b) Name an isomer of propan-2-ol.

c) A typical sterilising pad contains approximately 0.6 g of propan-2-ol. How many moles of propan-2-ol does a typical sterilising pad contain?

6 Esters are sweet-smelling liquids that are widely used as flavourings in various foods. For example, the ester ethyl ethanoate gives the distinctive taste associated with pear drop sweets.

a) Draw the full structural formula of ethyl ethanoate.

b) Esters are produced by reacting an alkanol with an alkanoic acid. Name the alkanol that was used to produce ethyl ethanoate.

c) Name the type of reaction that occurs to produce an ester.

7 Formic acid (methanoic acid) is contained in the stings of many insects such as wood ants and is also present in stinging nettles.

a) Draw the full structural formula of formic acid.

b) Ethyl methanoate is produced from methanoic acid and an alcohol. Name the alcohol.

c) Draw the full structural formula of ethyl methanoate.

Chapter 2.4
Combustion

Fuels are one of the most important substances on Earth. They provide the energy we need to live, such as by heating our homes and powering our cars. Combustion releases the energy that fuels contain.

When a substance burns it reacts with oxygen and this is known as combustion. All combustion reactions are exothermic because they release energy. For example, when methane is burned using a Bunsen burner, heat energy is given out. As combustion is the reaction of a fuel with oxygen, then it is obvious that oxygen must be present for combustion to take place. The oxygen required comes from the air.

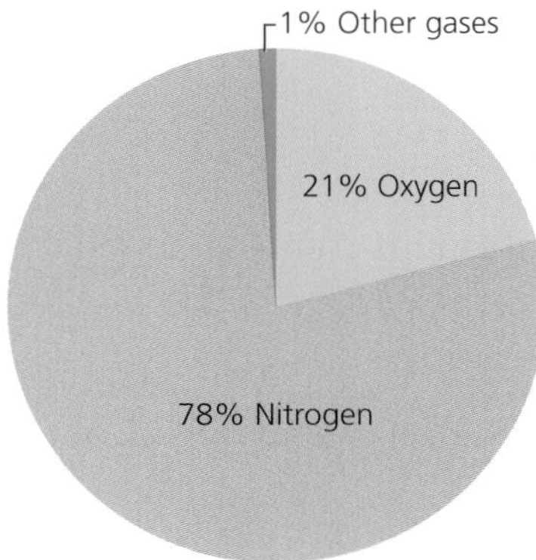

Figure 2.23 Only 21% of the air we breathe is oxygen, 78% is nitrogen and 1% other gases

For combustion to take place a fuel is required. Fuels are one of the most important substances on Earth. The energy they produce can be used to cook your food, heat your home, and keep cars and trains running. Without fuels the world would be a different place.

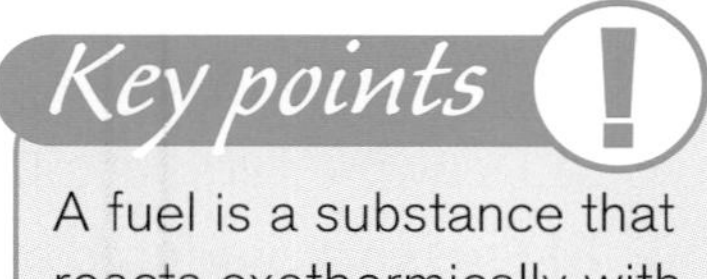

A fuel is a substance that reacts exothermically with oxygen.

Alkanes, alcohols and **carbohydrates** are all commonly used fuels. Alkanes such as methane are used to heat your home and cook your food. Alcohols such as ethanol can be used to power cars. In Brazil, ethanol is more commonly used than petrol to power 'FlexFuel' cars that can run on petrol or ethanol or a mixture of both. Carbohydrates such as glucose are used to power our bodies.

Figure 2.24 FlexFuel cars run on petrol and/or ethanol

Figure 2.25 Carbohydrates are fuels that power human bodies

Calculations involving balanced equations

Balanced equations can be used to predict the mass of a product produced by a chemical reaction or the mass of reactants required for the reaction.

Example

What mass of water is produced by combustion of 20 g of hydrogen gas?

To answer a question like this it is important to take it one step at a time.

1 Write out the balanced equation (see page 29 for a reminder of how to do this).

$$2H_2 + O_2 \rightarrow 2H_2O$$

2 Establish the molar ratio. It can be seen from the equation in step 1 that 2 moles of H_2 produce 2 moles of H_2O.

2 moles of hydrogen → 2 moles of water

2 → 2

(which is the same as) 1 → 1

3 Calculate the actual moles of hydrogen used and therefore the mass of water produced using the triangle shown below.

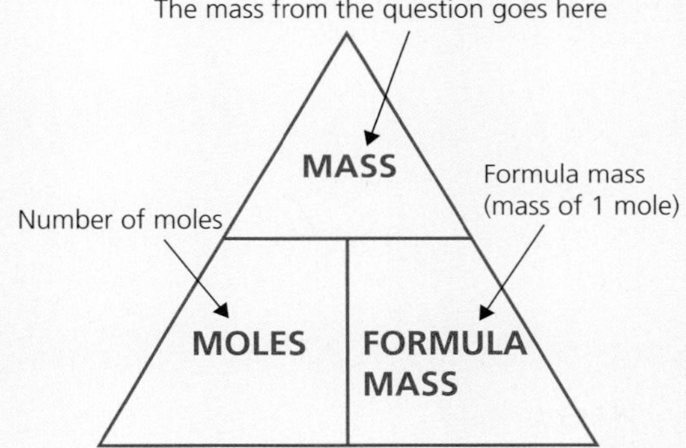

Moles of hydrogen burned	Molar ratio	Mass of water produced
$Moles = \frac{Mass}{FM}$ $= \frac{20}{2}$ $= 10$ *moles*	1 → 1 10 → 10	Mass = *moles* × *FM* = 10 × 18 = 180 g

180 g of water would be produced on combustion of 20 g of hydrogen.

Hints & tips

Remember that hydrogen gas is diatomic so the FM is 2 not 1!

Study questions

Go to page 54, where you will find questions for this topic.

Chapter 2.5 Enthalpy

When a chemical reaction takes place, there is usually a difference in energy between the reactants and products. This difference in energy is known as the enthalpy change. In this section we will revise what happens during exothermic and endothermic reactions and how to calculate the energy released or taken in by the reaction.

Most chemical reactions involve a change in energy, usually measured as a loss or gain of heat energy. The energy lost or gained is due to the difference in energy between the reactants and products. This difference in energy is known as the enthalpy change (E_h).

Exothermic reactions

An exothermic reaction is one in which heat energy is given out.

Because heat energy is released in **exothermic** reactions, this means that the products must have less energy than the reactants. This can be shown by a potential energy diagram.

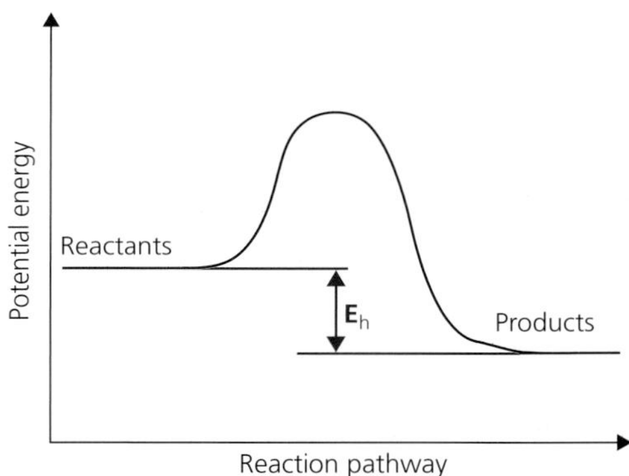

Figure 2.26 A potential energy diagram for an exothermic reaction where E_h is the energy difference between the reactants and the products. (Please note: potential energy diagrams do not form part of the National 5 Chemistry course but this diagram has been included to aid understanding of the topic.)

As can be seen from the graph in Figure 2.26, in all exothermic reactions the energy of the products is less than that of the reactants. Because energy has been lost, all exothermic reactions have a negative E_h.

$$\textit{exothermic reactions} = -E_h$$

Endothermic reactions

Key points

An endothermic reaction is one in which heat energy is taken in. This means that the products must have more energy than the reactants because energy has been absorbed.

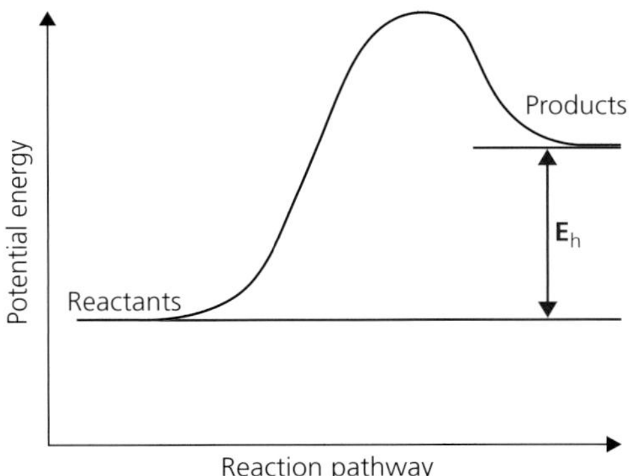

Figure 2.27 A potential energy diagram for an endothermic reaction where E_h is the energy difference between the reactants and the products. (Please note: potential energy diagrams do not form part of the National 5 Chemistry course but this diagram has been included to aid understanding of the topic.)

As can be seen from the graph in Figure 2.27, in all **endothermic** reactions the energy of the products is more than that of the reactants. Because energy has been gained, all endothermic reactions have a positive E_h.

$$\textit{endothermic reactions} = +E_h$$

Calculating enthalpy

An experiment can be carried out in the lab to establish the energy released on combustion of a substance using the apparatus shown in Figure 2.28.

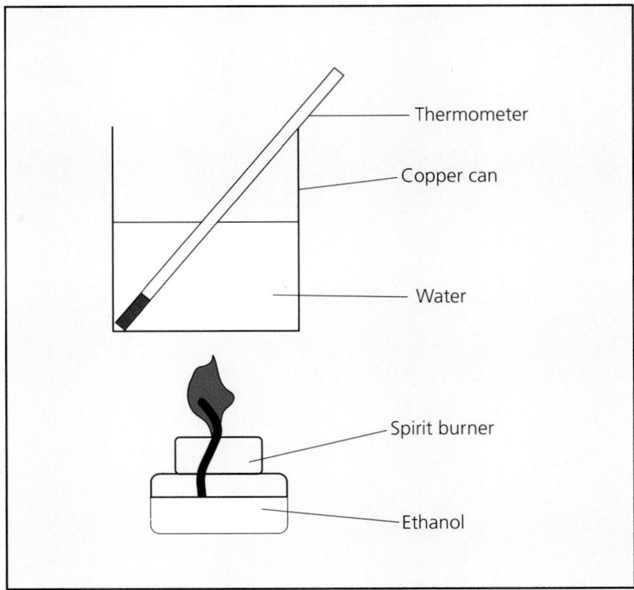

Figure 2.28 Apparatus used in the lab for establishing the energy released from the combustion of ethanol

Key points 

Combustion is an exothermic reaction and the energy that is released during combustion can be calculated using the equation shown below.

To calculate the enthalpy the following information must be recorded.

- The initial and final mass of the burner to establish the mass of alcohol burned.
- The initial and final temperatures of the water.
- The volume/mass of the water heated ($1\ cm^3 = 1\ g = 0.001\ kg$).

The enthalpy is then calculated using the equation:

$$E_h = cm\Delta T$$

Where:

- $\mathbf{E_h}$ is the energy change ($kJ\ mol^{-1}$)
- **c** is the specific heat capacity of water. It is a constant, $4.18\ kJ\ kg^{-1}\ °C^{-1}$
- **m** is the mass of water in kg ($100\ cm^3 = 0.1\ kg$). **Do not use the mass of fuel here!**
- **ΔT** is the change in temperature (°C).

Example 

The following data was recorded when ethanol (C_2H_5OH) was burned.

Data measured	Result
Mass of burner and ethanol before	52.65 g
Mass of burner and ethanol after	53.01 g
Mass of water heated	$200\ cm^3 = 0.2\ kg$
Initial temperature of water	21 °C
Final temperature of water	26 °C

Use the information above to calculate the energy change for this reaction.

Temperature change (ΔT) = 26 – 21 = 5 °C

$$E_h = cm\Delta T$$
$$= 4.18 \times 0.2 \times 5$$
$$= 4.18\ kJ$$

Study questions 

1 Oxygen gas is mixed with methane gas and ignited. What is the correct balanced equation for this reaction?

A $CH_4 + 2O_2 \rightarrow CO_2 + 2H_2O$

B $CH_4 + O_2 \rightarrow CO_2 + 2H_2O$

C $CH_4 + 2O_2 \rightarrow 2CO_2 + 2H_2O$

D $2CH_4 + 2O_2 \rightarrow 2CO_2 + 2H_2O$

⇨

2 The balanced equation for the complete combustion of a hydrocarbon X is shown below.

$X + 8O_2 \rightarrow 5CO_2 + 6H_2O$

Which of the following is the correct formula of hydrocarbon X?

A C_2H_6

B C_3H_8

C C_4H_{10}

D C_5H_{12}

3 Many chemical reactions involve energy changes and the energy released can be put to use.

a) Hand warmers make use of an increase in temperature that takes place during a reaction within the warmer. Name the type of reaction that results in an increase in temperature.

b) Flameless ration heaters are used by the armed forces to prepare meals when on missions. The energy released heats 330 g of water by 37.8 °C. Calculate the energy required to do this.

4 When 1 mole of propan-1-ol was burned, the temperature of 6 kg of water increased by 80 °C.
Using this information, what is the energy released by the combustion of propan-1-ol in kJ mol^{-1}?

5 What mass of carbon dioxide is produced on combustion of 32 g of methane gas?

$CH_4 + 2O_2 \rightarrow CO_2 + 2H_2O$

6 Iron(II) sulphate can be used in the treatment of anaemia. Iron(II) sulphate can be produced by reacting iron(II) oxide with sulphuric acid.

$FeO + H_2SO_4 \rightarrow FeSO_4 + H_2$

If 25 g of iron(II) oxide is reacted with excess sulphuric acid, what mass of iron(II) sulphate will be produced?

Unit 3 Chemistry and Society

Chapter 3.1
Metals

Over three-quarters of the elements known are metals – they appear on the left-hand side of the 'zigzag' line in the periodic table. In this section we will revise some reactions involving metals. We will begin by looking at why metals conduct electricity.

Metallic bonding

Metallic bonds occur between the atoms of metal elements. The outer electrons are delocalised (free to move). This produces an electrostatic force of attraction between the positive metal ions (atoms that have lost an electron to become positively charged) and the negative delocalised electrons, which acts as a glue holding the atoms together.

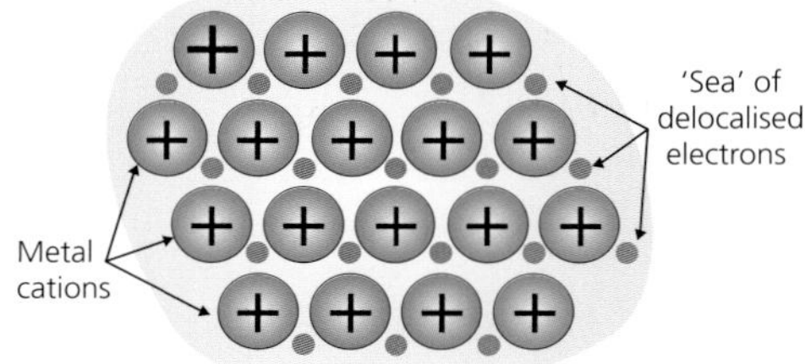

Figure 3.1 Metallic bonding

The delocalised electrons are the reason for metals being conductors of electricity. Electricity is a flow of electrons, so for a substance to conduct electricity it must allow electrons to flow through it and metals do this very well.

As one electron moves into the metal from the power supply, another will jump off the metal as shown in Figure 3.2.

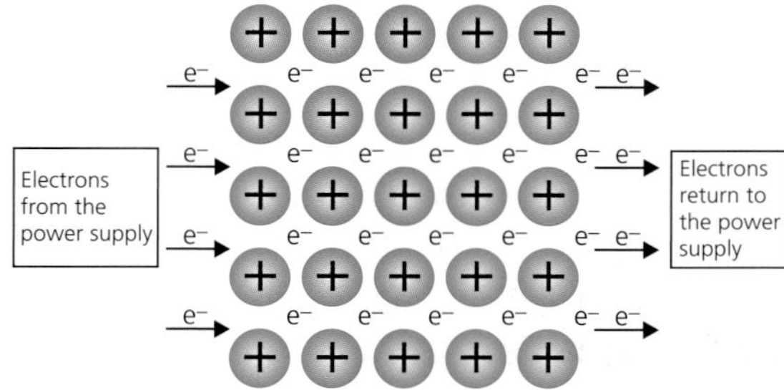

Figure 3.2 The conduction of electricity by a metal

Throughout this the metal remains completely unchanged as it always has the same amount of electrons.

Reactions of metals

Metals and water

Most metals don't react with water but some of the more reactive metals do. For example, the alkali metals lithium, sodium and potassium react very strongly and caesium can even explode in water.

reactive metal + water → metal hydroxide + hydrogen

Example 

Here is the equation and ionic equation for the reaction between lithium and water.

$$2Li(s) + 2H_2O(l) \rightarrow 2LiOH(aq) + H_2(g)$$

$$2Li(s) + 2H_2O(l) \rightarrow 2Li^+(aq) + 2OH^-(aq) + H_2(g)$$

Gold, silver and platinum don't react with water at all because they are unreactive metals.

Reactions with acids

As with water, it is the more reactive metals that will react with acids. Only the metals above hydrogen in the **reactivity series** will react with an acid because all acids contain H^+ ions. Acids will not have an effect on metals such as gold and platinum.

metal + acid → salt + hydrogen

Example 

Here is the equation and ionic equation for the reaction between magnesium and hydrochloric acid.

$$Mg(s) + 2HCl(aq) \rightarrow MgCl_2(aq) + H_2(g)$$

$$Mg(s) + 2H^+(aq) + 2Cl^-(aq) \rightarrow Mg^{2+}(aq) + 2Cl^-(aq) + H_2(g)$$

Reactions with oxygen

Again, only the most reactive metals react strongly with oxygen.

metal + oxygen → metal oxide

Example 

In class you may have burned magnesium. This reacts very strongly with oxygen to give off a bright light in a very exothermic reaction.

$$2Mg(s) + O_2(g) \rightarrow 2MgO(s)$$

The reactivity series

The reactions of metals make them very useful; one example of this is their use in batteries. Batteries provide electricity for our use. To understand how a battery works we must know what electricity is. Electricity is a flow of electrons that travel along wires.

In a battery this flow of electrons or electricity is produced by a chemical reaction taking place in the battery.

Batteries have one major disadvantage. They eventually run out. This happens when the chemicals in the battery are used up. Some batteries, however, are rechargeable, like the lead-acid battery.

Before we can learn how a battery works it helps to remind ourselves of the reactivity series. The reactivity series is a list of elements listed in order of reactivity starting with the most reactive. It is very similar to the electrochemical series in your data booklet but with a few differences.

There is an easy way to remember the reactivity series if you learn the following mnemonic.

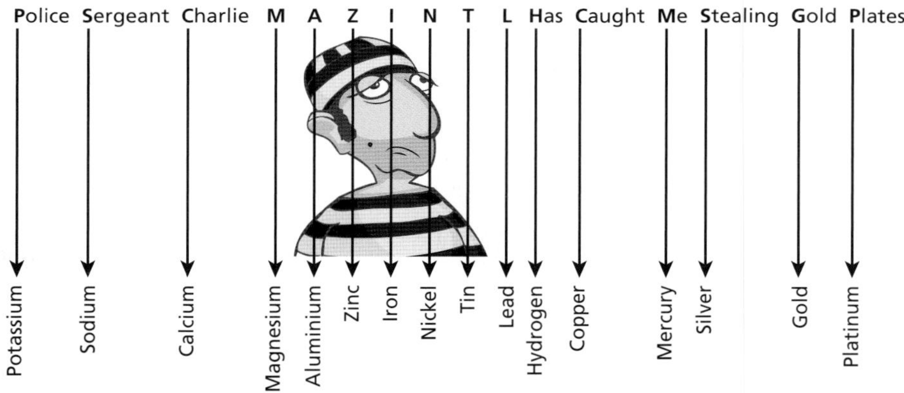

Figure 3.3

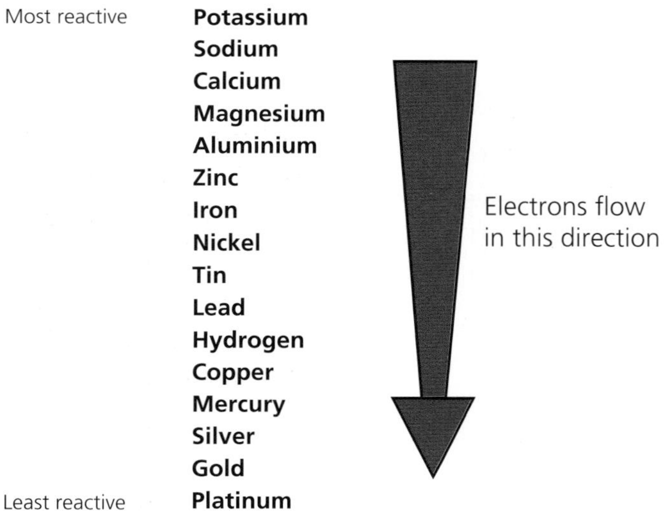

Figure 3.4 The reactivity series

What you should know

Cell story (part 1)

Magnesium and Copper are cowboys in the old Wild West. To win the heart of a fair lady they challenge each other to a 'shoot out' at high noon. They meet at noon, stand back-to-back, walk twelve paces and turn and shoot – BANG! Magnesium shoots Copper dead with a bullet and wins the lady. Magnesium was the fastest to REACT.

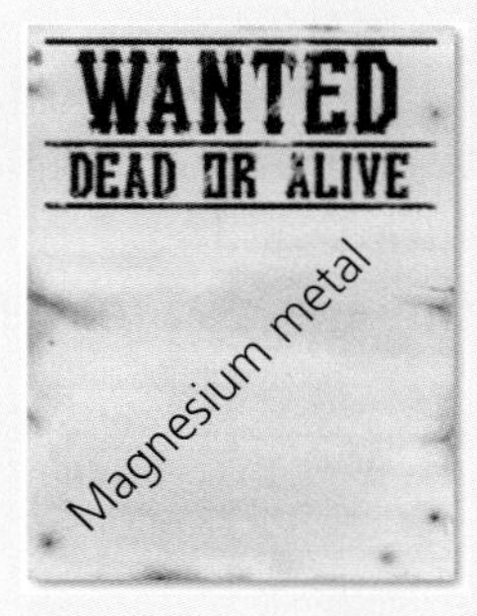

Hints & tips

*This story will make **cells** a lot easier to understand if you learn it!*

This story may seem out of place in a chemistry book but all will become clear when you read on.

The bullet in the story is a codeword for electrons. This means that the electrons are flowing from the magnesium (faster to react) to the copper (slower to react) through the wires.

The electrons (bullets) will always go from the most reactive metal to the least reactive metal (see Oxidation and reduction on page 62). Electricity is a flow of electrons, therefore electricity has been made when this happens.

Cells

In chemistry a battery is known as a **cell**. A cell is made up of two different metals connected by an **electrolyte**. An electrolyte is an ionic solution that is used to complete the circuit.

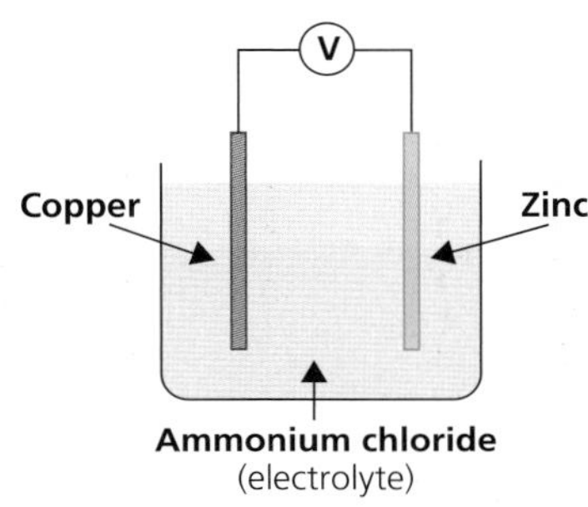

Figure 3.5 An example of a cell

Key points

* The flow of electrons in a cell is produced because of the difference in reactivity of the two metals.
* Electrons will flow from the most reactive metal (oxidation) to the least reactive metal (reduction).

Electrons in a cell will always flow from the most to the least reactive metal, so in the cell shown in Figure 3.5, the electrons will flow from the zinc to the copper because zinc is more reactive than copper.

The further apart the metals are in the electrochemical series the higher the voltage produced. So, in Figure 3.5, if we replaced the zinc in the cell with magnesium, the voltage produced by the cell would increase because the magnesium is even more reactive than zinc.

Hints & tips

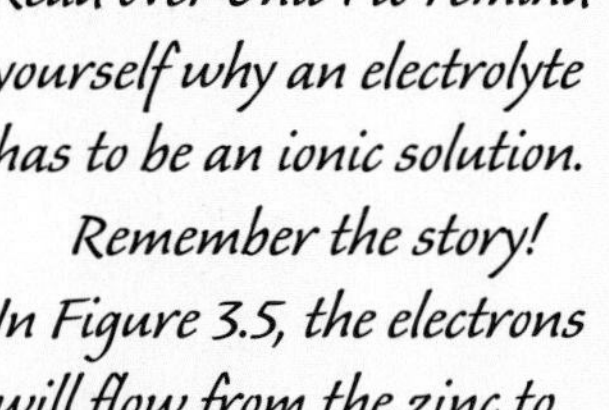

Read over Unit 1 to remind yourself why an electrolyte has to be an ionic solution.

Remember the story! In Figure 3.5, the electrons will flow from the zinc to the copper because zinc is faster to react than copper.

Different cells

There are several different ways in which cells can be made.

Electricity can also be produced in a cell by connecting two different metals in a solution of their own ions. In Figure 3.6, the electrons will flow from the zinc to the copper as in Figure 3.5. This will cause the zinc to dissolve and more copper to form on the surface of the copper electrode.

As with any electrical circuit it must be complete to work. The purpose of the **ion bridge** is to complete the circuit. The ion bridge is not some piece of high-tech electrical equipment. It is simply a piece of filter paper soaked in salt water or some other ionic solution.

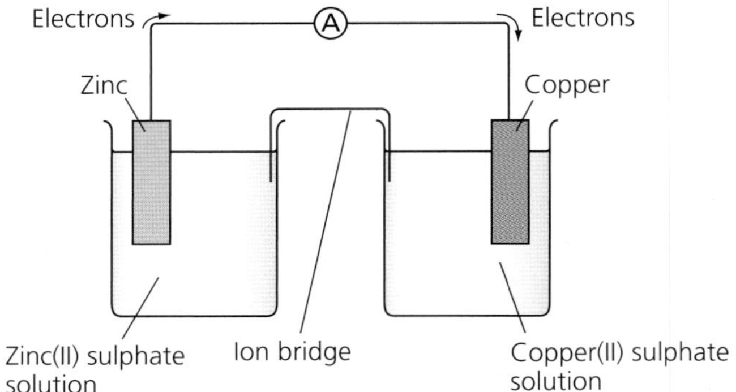

Figure 3.6 An example of a cell, the ion bridge completes the circuit

Another type of cell is one in which only one metal is involved and the other half of the cell contains SO_3^{2-} ions or I_2 with a carbon electrode. In these cells the electrons flow from the non-metal to the metal.

Fuel cells

A fuel cell is a device that converts chemical energy from a fuel such as hydrogen into electrical energy through a chemical reaction with oxygen or some other oxidising agent.

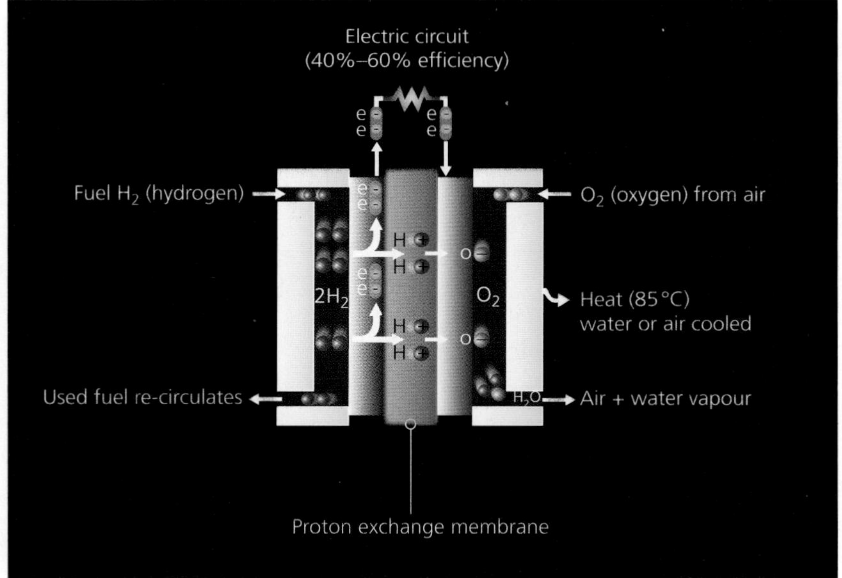

Figure 3.7 An example of a fuel cell

Batteries are built on the same type of electrochemical reactions as fuel cells are. The obvious difference is that a fuel cell requires an outside source of fuel, while batteries contain the chemicals that they require to produce electricity.

Rechargeable batteries

Batteries such as the zinc-carbon battery are non-rechargeable and when the chemicals are used up within the battery it should be recycled. Rechargeable batteries are different. Reversing the direction of electrical flow in a rechargeable battery reverses the chemical reaction that occurred in the battery in the first place making it ready for use again.

One example of a rechargeable battery is the lead-acid battery which is found in cars.

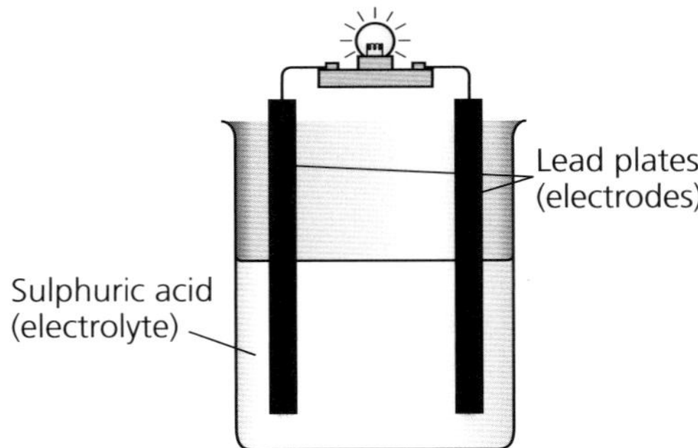

Figure 3.8 A lead-acid cell

Displacement reactions

What you should know

Cell story (part 2)

The story continues ......

After the 'shoot out' Magnesium (who was the winner) marries the lady and they live together happily ever after.

What this means is that the most reactive metal will ALWAYS win the lady. In chemistry terms, the most reactive metal will always combine with the lady, which is a group ion such as sulphate or nitrate.
This part of the story explains the concept of **displacement reactions**.

Key points

In displacement reactions a reactive metal displaces a metal that is less reactive from solution.

$$Mg(s) + CuSO_4(aq) \rightarrow MgSO_4(aq) + Cu(s)$$

This can be shown as an ionic equation:

$$Mg(s) + Cu^{2+}(aq) + SO_4^{2-}(aq) \rightarrow Mg^{2+}(aq) + SO_4^{2-}(aq) + Cu(s)$$

The most reactive metal always joins to the group ion (the non-metal) (SO_4 in this case).

If the group ion is already combined to the most reactive metal, then no reaction will occur. For example:

$$Pb + ZnSO_4 \rightarrow \text{no reaction}$$

When a metal reacts with acid, hydrogen is released (displaced). This is also a displacement reaction and can be used to place hydrogen in the electrochemical series.

Oxidation and reduction

Key points 

Substances can gain or lose electrons.

* When substances lose electrons it is known as oxidation.
* When substances gain electrons it is known as reduction.

Hints & tips

There is an easy way to remember this key point using an Oil Rig.

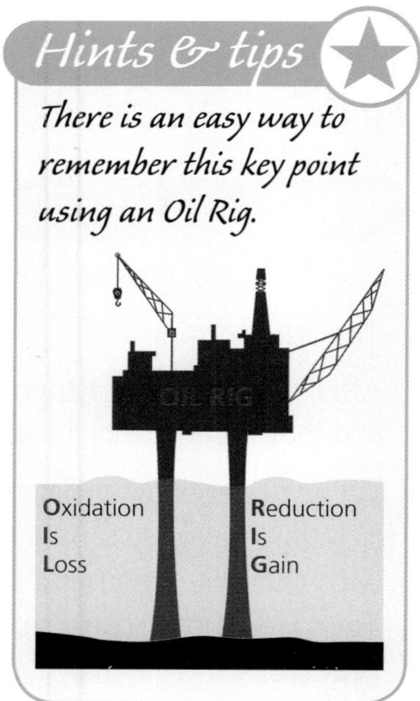

When a metal element is reacting to form a compound then it is being oxidised. In the following equation, the magnesium is losing two electrons so it is an **oxidation reaction**:

$$Mg \rightarrow Mg^{2+} + 2e^-$$

A **reduction reaction** is the opposite of oxidation. It is the gaining of electrons. For example,

$$Cu^{2+} + 2e^- \rightarrow Cu$$

A **redox reaction** is one where both oxidation and reduction take place. All displacement reactions are redox reactions because one metal is gaining electrons (reduction) and one metal is losing electrons (oxidation).

These equations can be used to illustrate the loss and gain of electrons in a cell. If the cell involved magnesium and copper, the magnesium would lose electrons (oxidation reaction) and the copper would gain the electrons (reduction reaction). Therefore a cell is another example of a redox reaction.

Extraction of metals

When metals are found in nature they have been there for a very long time. This means that they have probably reacted with the oxygen in the air and water. Most of them are not discovered as a pure metal but as a compound. When metals are found in this state they are called **ores**.

The less reactive metals such as gold and platinum are found as a pure metal because they are very unreactive. All the other metals have to be removed from their ores. The more reactive the metal, the more difficult it is to remove.

The table below shows the processes which must be undertaken to remove metals from their ores.

Metal	Process by which metal is extracted from ores
Potassium	electrolysis
Sodium	
Lithium	
Calcium	
Magnesium	
Aluminium	
Zinc	Heat plus carbon or carbon monoxide
Iron	Blast furnace
Tin	Heat plus carbon or carbon monoxide
Lead	
Copper	
Mercury	Heat alone
Silver	
Gold	

The less reactive metals are removed from their ores simply by heating; however, some need to be heated with a reducing agent such as carbon or carbon monoxide to remove the oxygen. A reducing agent is a substance that can donate electrons.

The more reactive metals require **electrolysis** to remove the impurities. Iron, however, is removed in a **blast furnace**.

Study questions

1 Metallic bonds are due to:

A an attraction between positive ions and delocalised electrons

B a shared pair of electrons

C an attraction between positive ions and negative ions

D an attraction between negative ions and delocalised electrons

2 $Fe^{2+} + e^{-} \rightarrow Fe^{+}(aq)$

This ion electron equation represents the:

A reduction of iron(II) ions

B reduction of iron(I) ions

C oxidation of iron(II) ions

D oxidation of iron(I) ions

3 Which pair of metals will produce an electron flow in the direction shown in Figure 3.9?

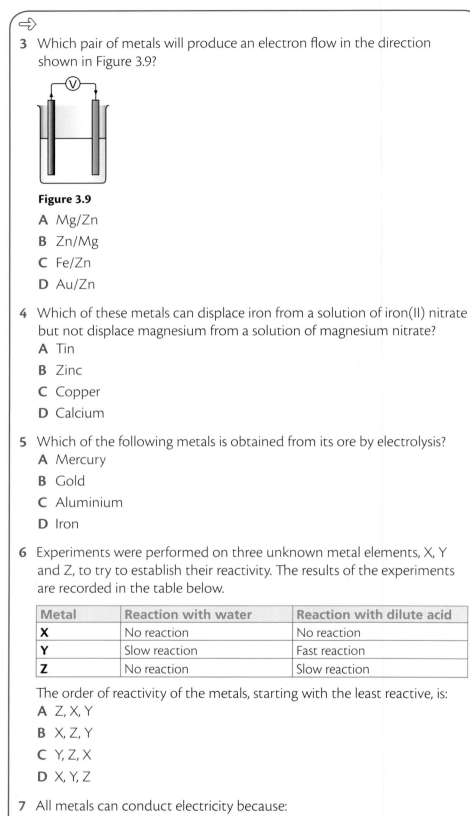

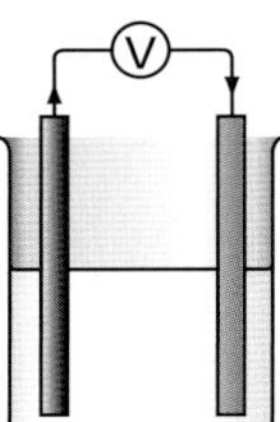

Figure 3.9

A Mg/Zn

B Zn/Mg

C Fe/Zn

D Au/Zn

4 Which of these metals can displace iron from a solution of iron(II) nitrate but not displace magnesium from a solution of magnesium nitrate?

A Tin

B Zinc

C Copper

D Calcium

5 Which of the following metals is obtained from its ore by electrolysis?

A Mercury

B Gold

C Aluminium

D Iron

6 Experiments were performed on three unknown metal elements, X, Y and Z, to try to establish their reactivity. The results of the experiments are recorded in the table below.

Metal	Reaction with water	Reaction with dilute acid
X	No reaction	No reaction
Y	Slow reaction	Fast reaction
Z	No reaction	Slow reaction

The order of reactivity of the metals, starting with the least reactive, is:

A Z, X, Y

B X, Z, Y

C Y, Z, X

D X, Y, Z

7 All metals can conduct electricity because:

A the electricity breaks the bonds between the atoms

B the outer energy level electrons in metals are free to move

C the shared electrons between the atoms attract stray protons

D the metals contain mobile ions

8 In Figure 3.10 what is the purpose of the ion bridge?

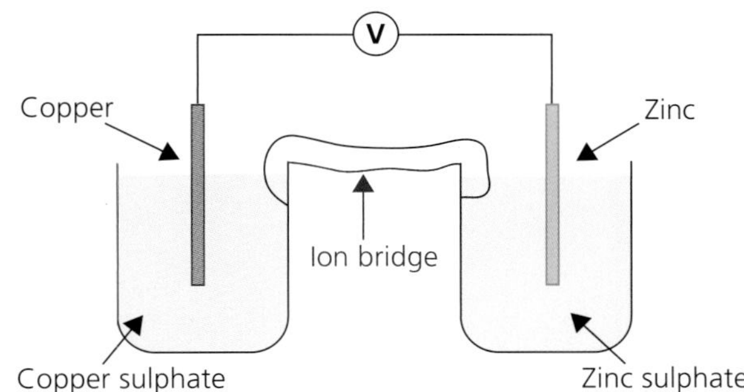

Figure 3.10

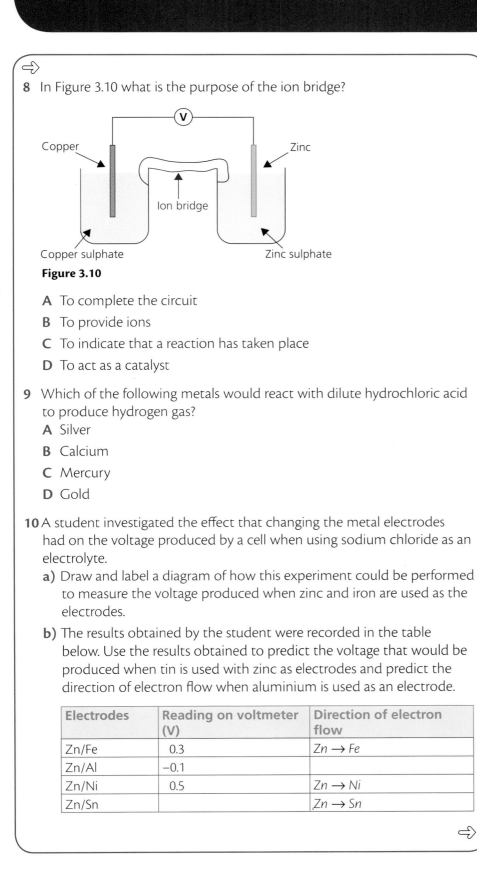

A To complete the circuit
B To provide ions
C To indicate that a reaction has taken place
D To act as a catalyst

9 Which of the following metals would react with dilute hydrochloric acid to produce hydrogen gas?
A Silver
B Calcium
C Mercury
D Gold

10 A student investigated the effect that changing the metal electrodes had on the voltage produced by a cell when using sodium chloride as an electrolyte.

a) Draw and label a diagram of how this experiment could be performed to measure the voltage produced when zinc and iron are used as the electrodes.

b) The results obtained by the student were recorded in the table below. Use the results obtained to predict the voltage that would be produced when tin is used with zinc as electrodes and predict the direction of electron flow when aluminium is used as an electrode.

Electrodes	Reading on voltmeter (V)	Direction of electron flow
Zn/Fe	0.3	$Zn \rightarrow Fe$
Zn/Al	−0.1	
Zn/Ni	0.5	$Zn \rightarrow Ni$
Zn/Sn		$Zn \rightarrow Sn$

11 The experiment shown in Figure 3.11 to list the metals copper, magnesium and zinc in order of reactivity was performed by reacting each of the metals with oxygen gas.

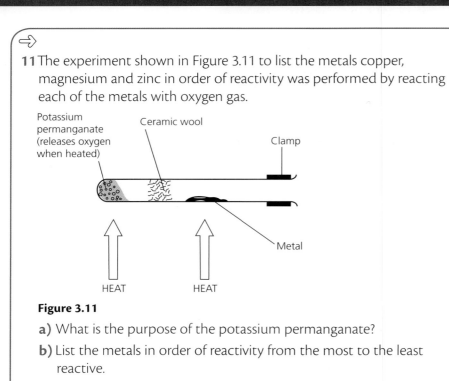

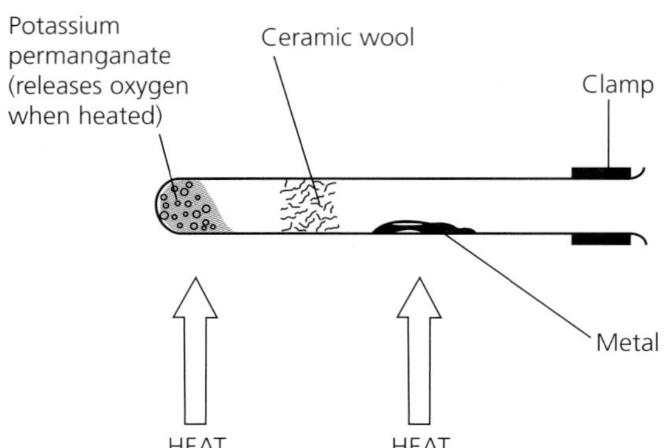

Figure 3.11

a) What is the purpose of the potassium permanganate?

b) List the metals in order of reactivity from the most to the least reactive.

12 When copper is added to a solution of silver nitrate the solution turns blue and the copper turns from brown to silver.

$$2AgNO_3(aq) + Cu(s) \rightarrow Cu(NO_3)_2(aq) + 2Ag(s)$$

a) Name the type of reaction that is taking place.

b) Name the spectator ion in this reaction.

c) What does this reaction suggest about the reactivity of silver in comparison to copper?

d) Write the ion-electron equation for the oxidation step in this reaction.

Chapter 3.2

Properties of Plastics

There are many different types of plastics all with very different properties. This gives them a massive range of uses from clothing to packaging to children's toys. In this section we will revise the advantages and disadvantages of plastics as well as looking at how plastics are produced.

Natural or synthetic?

Synthetic is the name given to all materials that are man-made. All plastics are synthetic compounds made mainly from the crude oil fraction, naphtha.

There are many advantages of plastics over natural materials and some disadvantages. For example, cotton (natural) is far more comfortable to wear but nylon (synthetic) is far more hardwearing.

Plastics are made by a process called **polymerisation** of which there are two types – **addition polymerisation** and **condensation polymerisation**.

Addition polymerisation

Polymerisation is a process by which many small molecules called monomers combine to form one large molecule called a **polymer** (the plastic).

Key points 

- Monomers are the small molecules that combine to form a polymer.
- A polymer is the large molecule formed by combining many monomer molecules.

In Unit 2 we learned about addition reactions with alkenes and bromine. The concept is the same for addition polymerisation but on a much larger scale.

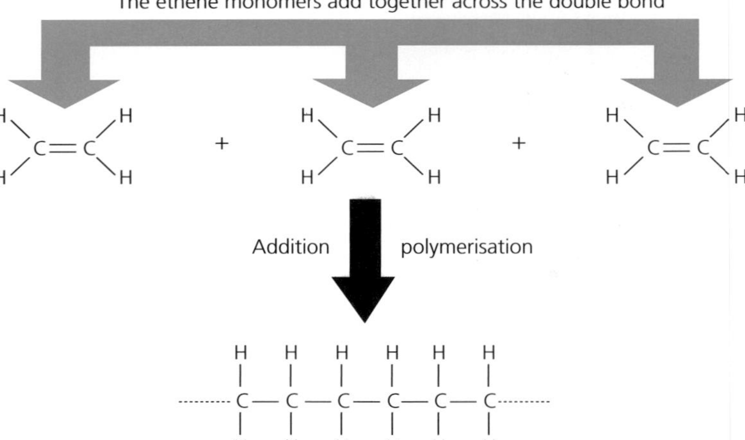

Figure 3.12 An example of addition polymerisation of ethene

In the example shown in Figure 3.12 the ethene monomers add to each other across the double bond to form the polymer polyethene, or polythene as it is commonly known. Because addition polymerisation is the addition of monomer molecules across their double bonds, then for this process to work, the monomers for addition polymerisation must be unsaturated.

Naming the polymer produced is very simple – add poly to the start of the monomer name. So:

- ethene produces poly(ethene)
- propene produces poly(propene).

Note the open bonds at both ends of the polymer shown in Figure 3.12. This indicates that the polymer shown is just a small section of the polymer and this section continues on. Because the polymer molecules produced are very large, chemists have developed what is known as the repeating unit. This is a shortened version of the polymer molecule which makes things a bit simpler. Some examples are shown in Figures 3.13 and 3.14 where 'n' is any large number.

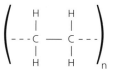

Figure 3.13 The repeating unit for poly(ethene)

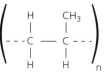

Figure 3.14 The repeating unit for poly(propene)

Condensation polymerisation

Condensation polymerisation is similar to addition polymerisation in that many small monomer molecules combine to form a polymer. The difference is that during condensation polymerisation, water or other small molecules such as hydrogen chloride are also produced.

Howdy it's Cowboy John! Use my lasso again to remove the water, same as when we looked at esters. YEE-HAW!

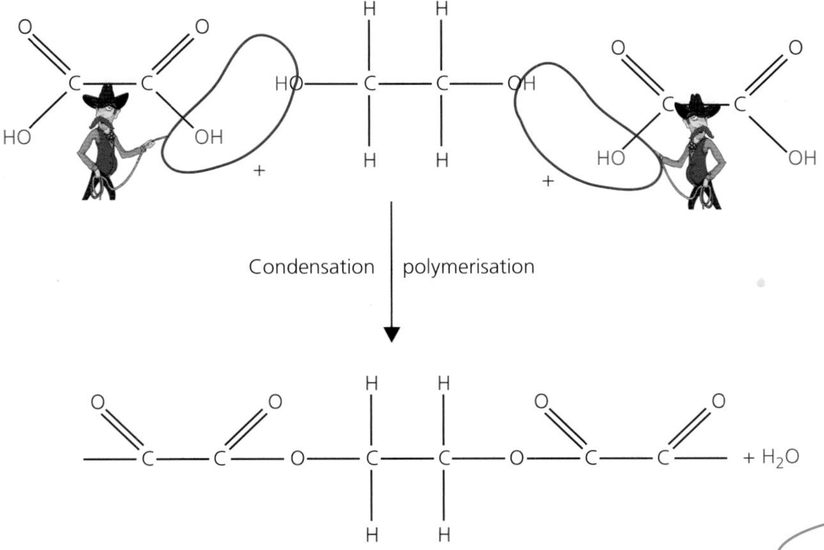

Figure 3.15 An example of condensation polymerisation

My name is Ester and I am a COO!

The condensation polymer shown in Figure 3.15 is classed as a polyester because it has the ester functional group. Note that during condensation polymerisation the OHs on the ends are also removed, because many monomers will combine to make the polymer not just the three monomers shown.

Polyester and nylon are examples of synthetic condensation polymers, but there are also natural condensation polymers such as starch and proteins. Starch is a natural condensation polymer formed by the combination of many glucose molecules.

The monomers used to make a polymer through condensation polymerisation can be identified from the structure of the polymer by breaking the polymer across the functional group. You may be asked in the exam to identify whether a polymer is produced by condensation or addition polymerisation. To answer this, look at the functional groups of the monomers. If they have a double carbon to carbon bond, the polymer is likely to have been produced by addition polymerisation.

Example 1

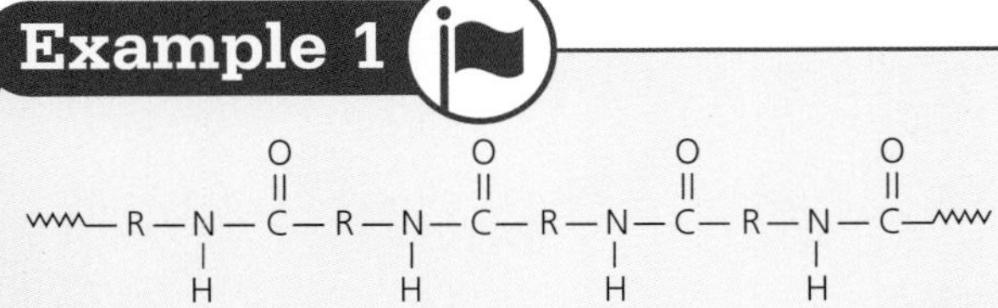

Figure 3.16 A polyamide molecule

The polyamide molecule shown in Figure 3.16 is a condensation polymer. When this compound is broken down or hydrolysed (opposite of condensation) a carboxyl functional group will be formed and water is required to do this.

Example 2

```
 H    H    H    H    H    H    H    H
 |    |    |    |    |    |    |    |
—C —  C —  C —  C —  C —  C —  C —  C—
 |    |    |    |    |    |    |    |
 H   CH3   H   CH3   H   CH3   H   CH3
```

Figure 3.17

The polymer shown in Figure 3.17 is an addition polymer. To break this back up into the monomers that made it, simply find the repeating unit and add a double bond so that each carbon has formed four bonds.

```
 /  H    H  \            H    H
|   |    |   |           |    |
| —C  —  C — |           C ═  C
|   |    |   |           |    |
 \  H   CH3 / n          H   CH3
```

Repeating unit   Monomer

Figure 3.18

The monomer used to produce polypropylene is propene.

Study questions

Go to page 75 for study questions on this topic.

Chapter 3.3

Fertilisers

Fertilisers are required for the production of crops. Year on year the world population is increasing and this has led to a bigger demand on food production. This has resulted in the need for fertilisers that are capable of producing the food required to meet these high demands. In this section you will revise what a fertiliser is and how they are produced.

What is a fertiliser?

Fertilisers provide the three main nutrients that plants require to grow well. The three main nutrients are:

- nitrogen (N)
- phosphorous (P)
- potassium (K).

There are two main types of fertiliser:

- Natural fertilisers such as manure and compost provide mainly nitrogen compounds.
- Synthetic (man-made) fertilisers provide all three nutrients in varying amounts. They can be expensive.

Ammonia (NH_3)

Ammonia is a very important chemical. It is used as a fertiliser, and can also be used to make other fertilisers, as well as explosives, medicines and cleaning products. Ammonia is an alkaline gas with a very unpleasant smell.

Ammonia is very soluble in water. The solubility of ammonia can be demonstrated by performing the 'Ammonia Fountain' experiment shown in Figure 3.20.

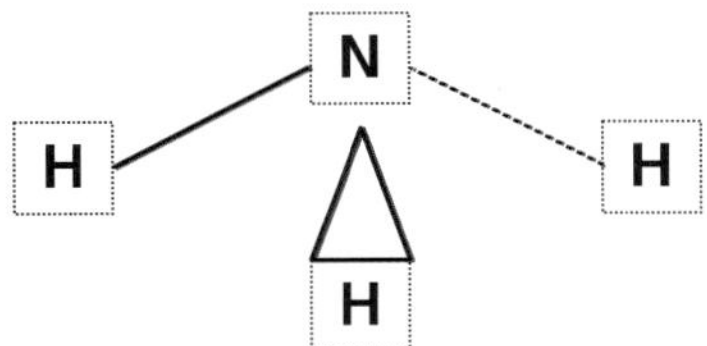
N
H
H
H

Figure 3.19 Ammonia

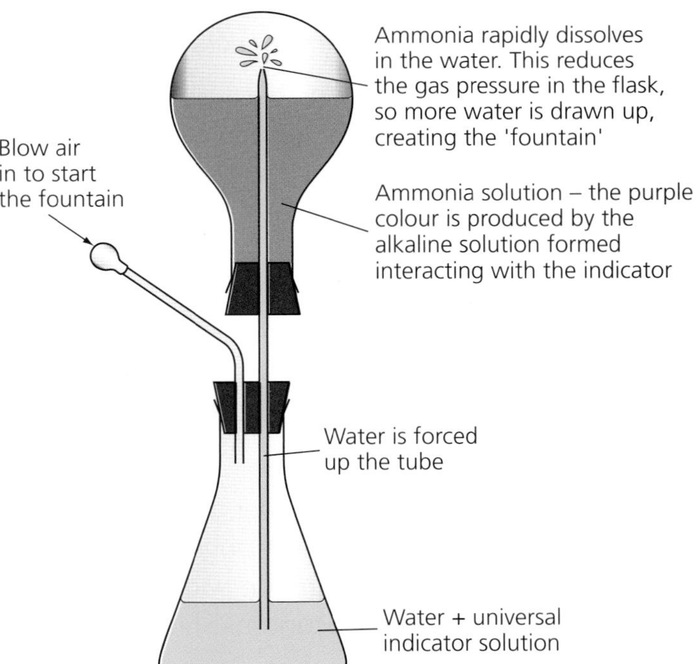
Ammonia rapidly dissolves in the water. This reduces the gas pressure in the flask, so more water is drawn up, creating the 'fountain'
Blow air in to start the fountain
Ammonia solution – the purple colour is produced by the alkaline solution formed interacting with the indicator
Water is forced up the tube
Water + universal indicator solution

Figure 3.20 The 'Ammonia Fountain' experiment

Ammonia can be prepared in the lab by heating an ammonium salt with an alkali such as sodium hydroxide:

$$NH_4Cl(s) + NaOH(aq) \rightarrow NH_3(g) + NaCl(s) + H_2O(l)$$

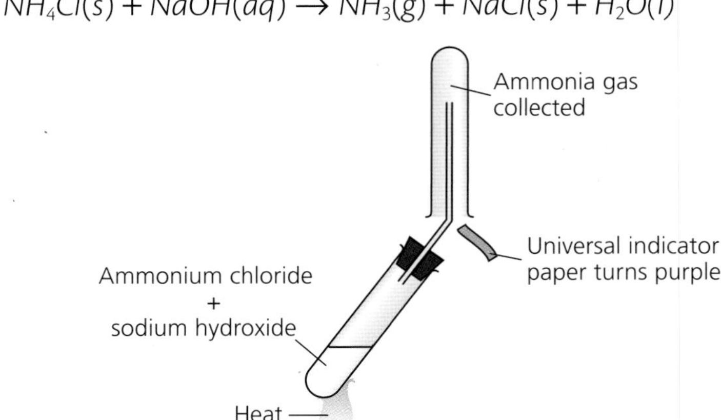

Figure 3.21 Ammonia being prepared in the laboratory

In industry, ammonia is produced by the **Haber process**.

The Haber process

The Haber process produces ammonia (NH_3) by combining nitrogen and hydrogen. The nitrogen required comes from the air and the hydrogen from steam or methane. They are converted into ammonia by passing them over an iron catalyst at a moderately high temperature of 400 °C using a pressure of 200 atmospheres.

These conditions are chosen because at low temperatures the reaction is very slow. However, at high temperatures the ammonia breaks down back into hydrogen and nitrogen because the reaction is reversible.

$$N_2(g) + 3H_2(g) \rightleftharpoons 2NH_3(g)$$

The yield of ammonia is greatest at high pressures but this is very expensive so a pressure of 200 atmospheres is used.

The iron catalyst speeds up the rate of the reaction and is broken down into small pieces to increase its surface area and therefore its effectiveness as a catalyst.

When all these conditions are set the yield of ammonia will only be approximately 15%, so all the nitrogen and hydrogen that are not converted into ammonia are put back into the reaction chamber to make the whole process more economic. Nothing is wasted. This can be seen in Figure 3.22.

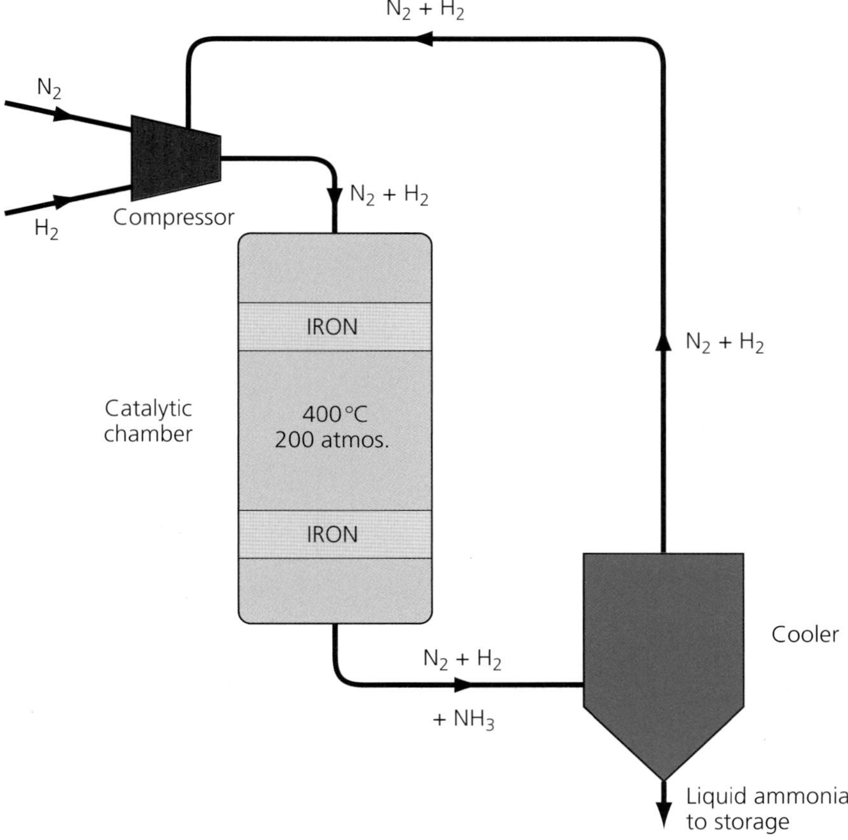

Figure 3.22 The Haber process

The ammonia produced by the Haber process can be used to produce nitric acid, which in turn can be used to produce ammonium nitrate.

The Ostwald process

Producing nitric acid in the lab is a difficult process because nitrogen is very unreactive due to its strong triple bond. It can be done by sparking air, like the spark plugs in a car engine, but this is very expensive. (The same process happens naturally in lightning storms.) The more economic way is by the **Ostwald process**.

The Ostwald process involves passing ammonia (from the Haber process) and air over a platinum catalyst at a high temperature of 800 °C. This produces nitrogen monoxide which combines with oxygen to form nitrogen dioxide. This can easily be converted into nitric acid by dissolving in water.

The Ostwald process is an exothermic reaction, so once the reaction is started the heat can be removed and the catalyst will continue to glow red hot.

Ammonium nitrate

Ammonium nitrate is a very important fertiliser because it contains 34% nitrogen. It won't break down easily and release its nitrogen into the atmosphere when stored but it has to be stored carefully as it can be very explosive. This was seen in Texas in 1947, when a fire on board the

SS Grandcamp detonated 2.5 tonnes of ammonium nitrate and the resulting fires and explosions killed 581 people.

Ammonium nitrate is produced by reacting ammonia with nitric acid.

$$NH_3(l) + HNO_3(aq) \rightarrow NH_4NO_3(aq)$$

This reaction is violent and highly exothermic. The ammonium nitrate produced is mostly used as a fertiliser but can also be used to produce explosives.

Percentage composition calculations

The percentage of elements in a compound can be calculated using the following.

$$\text{percentage composition} = \frac{\text{mass of element} \times 100}{\text{formula mass}}$$

This is called percentage composition.

Example

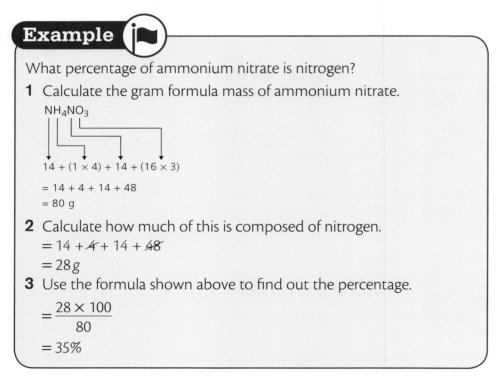

What percentage of ammonium nitrate is nitrogen?

1 Calculate the gram formula mass of ammonium nitrate.

NH_4NO_3

$14 + (1 \times 4) + 14 + (16 \times 3)$

$= 14 + 4 + 14 + 48$

$= 80\text{ g}$

2 Calculate how much of this is composed of nitrogen.

$= 14 + \cancel{4} + 14 + \cancel{48}$

$= 28\text{g}$

3 Use the formula shown above to find out the percentage.

$= \frac{28 \times 100}{80}$

$= 35\%$

Study questions ?

1 The Haber process produces ammonia (NH_3) by combining nitrogen and hydrogen.

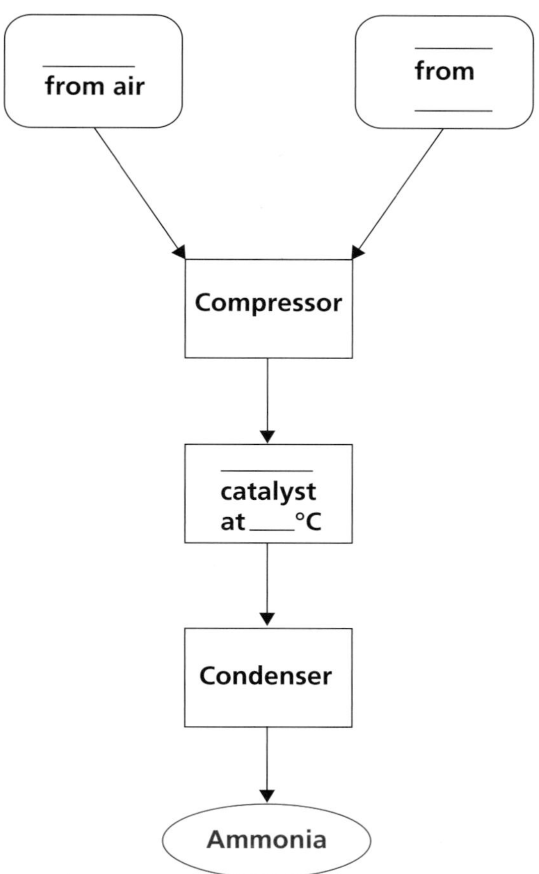

a) Complete the flow diagram using the following word list: **iron, nitrogen, hydrogen, 400, methane**.

b) Add a line to the flow diagram to show the unreacted hydrogen and nitrogen being recycled.

2 Kevlar was a polymer that was developed in 1965 and was first used in the tyres of racing cars to give them strength. It is also used as body armour.

Figure 3.23 shows the reaction performed to produce Kevlar. What type of reaction is this?

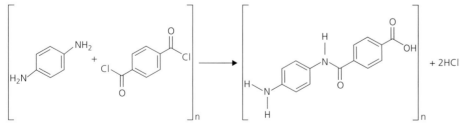

Figure 3.23

3 Poly(ethanol) is a water soluble plastic that has many uses from laundry bags to dishwasher tablets.

a) Plastics are synthetic. What is meant by the term 'synthetic'?

b) When heated, poly(ethanol) softens and can be reshaped. What name is given to such plastics?

4 Styrene, which is also known as phenylethene, can be extracted from the sap of the styrax tree. Styrene is the monomer used to produce polystyrene.

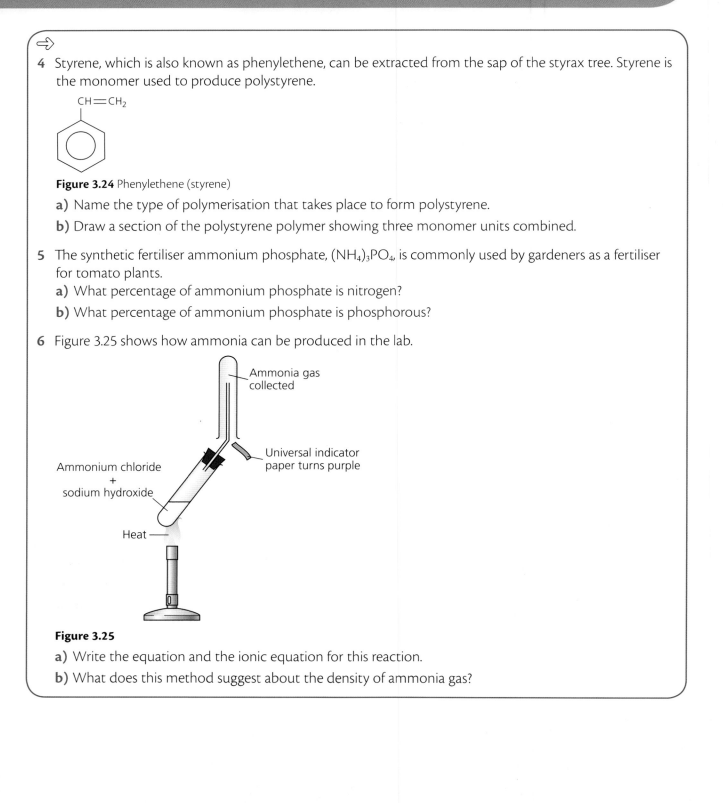

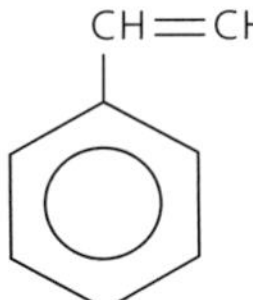

Figure 3.24 Phenylethene (styrene)

a) Name the type of polymerisation that takes place to form polystyrene.

b) Draw a section of the polystyrene polymer showing three monomer units combined.

5 The synthetic fertiliser ammonium phosphate, $(NH_4)_3PO_4$, is commonly used by gardeners as a fertiliser for tomato plants.

a) What percentage of ammonium phosphate is nitrogen?

b) What percentage of ammonium phosphate is phosphorous?

6 Figure 3.25 shows how ammonia can be produced in the lab.

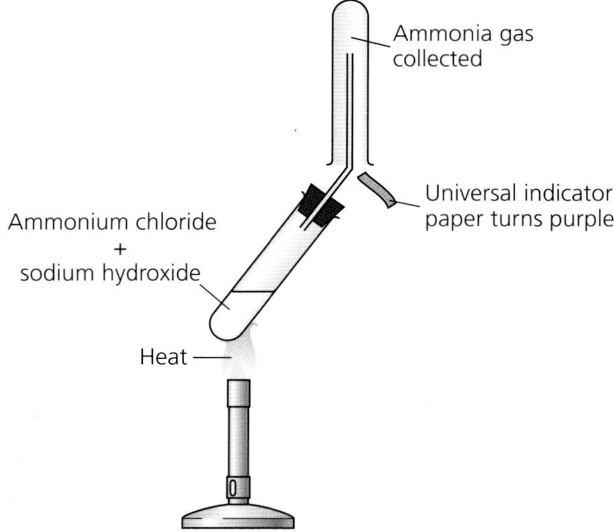

Figure 3.25

a) Write the equation and the ionic equation for this reaction.

b) What does this method suggest about the density of ammonia gas?

Chapter 3.4

Nuclear Chemistry

In 1896, French scientist Henri Becquerel discovered that compounds of uranium had an effect on photographic plates from a distance. The radiation they emitted could also penetrate opaque materials. The phenomenon was called radioactivity. In this section we will revise the properties of the three types of radiation, how to calculate the half-life of a radioactive element and the different uses of radioisotopes.

Radioactivity

Radioactivity is the result of unstable nuclei emitting energy or a particle to form more stable nuclei. There are three types of radiation:

- alpha (α)
- beta (β)
- gamma (γ).

Each type of radioactivity has different properties.

Alpha particles

$^{4}_{2}He^{2+}$

Alpha particles are slow moving, positively charged particles that come from the nucleus of a radioactive element. They consist of two protons and two neutrons and have a 2+ charge. Alpha particles have little penetration and will be stopped by a few cm of air or a sheet of paper.

The nuclear equation below shows an example of nuclear decay with the emission of an alpha particle.

$$^{232}_{90}Th \rightarrow\, ^{228}_{88}Ra + \,^{4}_{2}He^{2+}$$

Hints & tips

In nuclear equations the mass numbers and atomic numbers on each side of the equation must balance.

Beta particles

$^{0}_{-1}e^{-}$

Beta particles are electrons. They are fast moving, negatively charged particles that are formed when a neutron from the nucleus splits into a proton and an electron. They have greater penetration than an alpha particle and can pass through air but they cannot penetrate thin metal foil.

The nuclear equation for beta decay creates a product with an atomic number that has increased but the mass number is unchanged. For example:

$$^{228}_{88}Ra \rightarrow\, ^{228}_{89}Ac + \,^{0}_{-1}e$$

Gamma waves

Gamma radiation is non-particulate. This means that it is not a particle like alpha or beta radiation but a form of electromagnetic radiation of high energy. The gamma waves are emitted from the nucleus of a radioactive element.

The non-particulate nature of gamma waves means that they do not change the nature of the atom, so there are no nuclear equations for gamma radiation.

Gamma radiation has the greatest penetration of the three types of radioactivity and thick lead or concrete is required to absorb gamma rays.

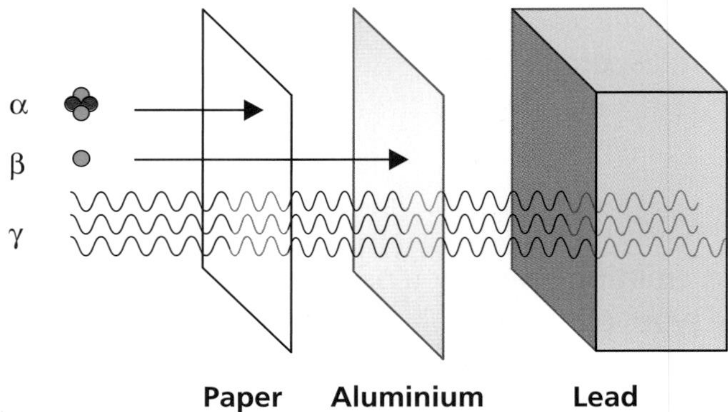

Figure 3.26 This diagram illustrates the penetration of each of the three types of radioactivity

The nature of each type of radiation can be demonstrated by passing them through a magnetic field (Figure 3.27).

- The beta particle $_{-1}^{0}e$ is negatively charged and therefore it is attracted to the positively charged plate.
- The alpha particle $_{2}^{4}He^{2+}$ is positively charged and therefore it is attracted to the negatively charged plate.
- Gamma waves have no charge because they are non-particulate and are therefore not affected by any of the charged plates.

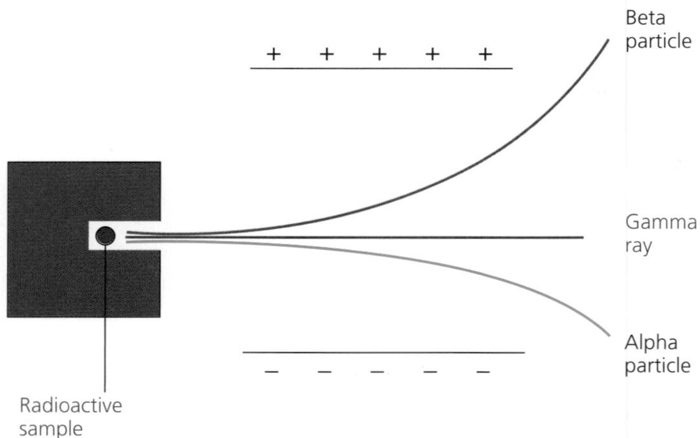

Figure 3.27 The effect that a magnetic field has on radioactive particles

Half-life

The decay of a radioactive element is independent of physical or chemical factors. This means that the breakdown of unstable nuclei is not affected by temperature, pressure, concentration, mass or chemical state.

However, it is possible to accurately calculate the time taken for the activity or mass of a radioactive element to drop by half. The time taken to do this is called the **half-life** of the isotope. Calculating half-life is relatively straightforward as you can see in the following example.

Example

The mass of a radioisotope falls from 3.2 g to 0.2 g in 3 hours. What is the half-life of this radioisotope?

$$\textit{Original mass} = 3.2 \xrightarrow{1} 1.6 \xrightarrow{2} 0.8 \xrightarrow{3} 0.4 \xrightarrow{4} 0.2$$

The mass has halved four times in 3 hours so the half-life is

$\frac{3}{4} = 0.75$ *hours.*

Because isotopes decay at a known rate they can be used to accurately date materials. For example, ${}^{14}_{6}C$ is used to date archaeological specimens up to 10 000 years old. This is illustrated in the half-life graph shown in Figure 3.28.

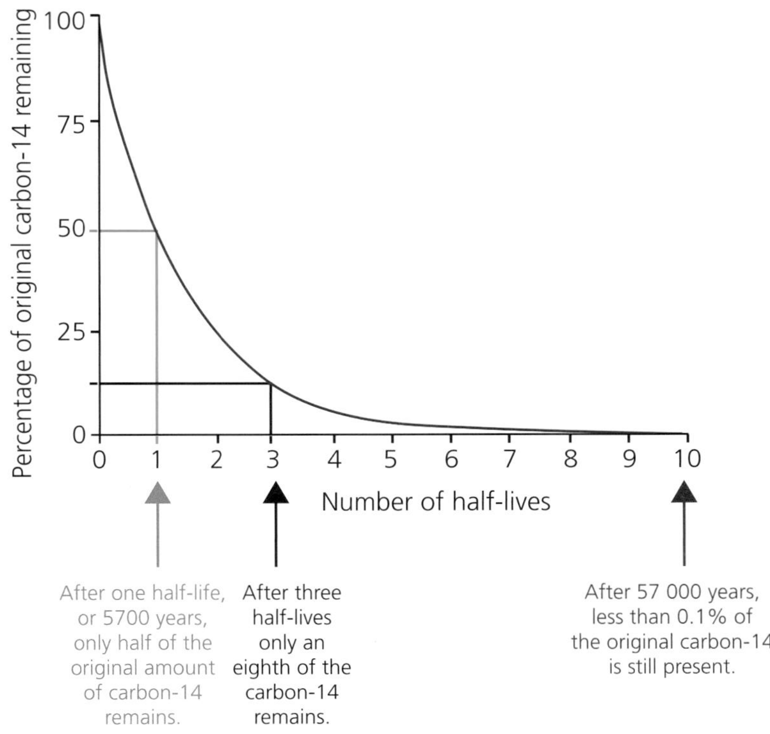
Percentage of original carbon-14 remaining
100
75
50
25
0
0
1
2
3
4
5
6
7
8
9
10
Number of half-lives
After one half-life, or 5700 years, only half of the original amount of carbon-14 remains.
After three half-lives only an eighth of the carbon-14 remains.
After 57 000 years, less than 0.1% of the original carbon-14 is still present.

Figure 3.28 Half-life graph

Uses of radioisotopes

The uses of radioisotopes in different fields such as medicine and industry are constantly expanding. A few are listed below.

- Radioisotopes can be used in the treatment of cancer. Gamma emitter cobalt-60 is used for the treatment of tumours and the less-penetrating beta emitter phosphorous-32 can be used in the treatment of skin cancer.

- Leaks in pipelines can be investigated by using radioisotopes with a short half-life. The radiation emitted can be detected if a leak is present.
- Americium-241 is used in domestic smoke alarms. Small amounts of smoke can affect the amount of radiation passing through a small gap and an alarm is triggered.
- Nuclear power stations provide approximately 50% of Scotland's electricity.

Figure 3.29 Torness Nuclear Power Station

Study questions 

1 Radioactive iodine-131 is a very effective treatment of cancer of the thyroid gland. Iodine-131 differs from the stable isotopes of iodine in:

A atomic number

B atomic mass

C chemical properties

D valency

2 There are three types of radioactive decay, all of which can be stopped in different ways as shown in Figure 3.30.

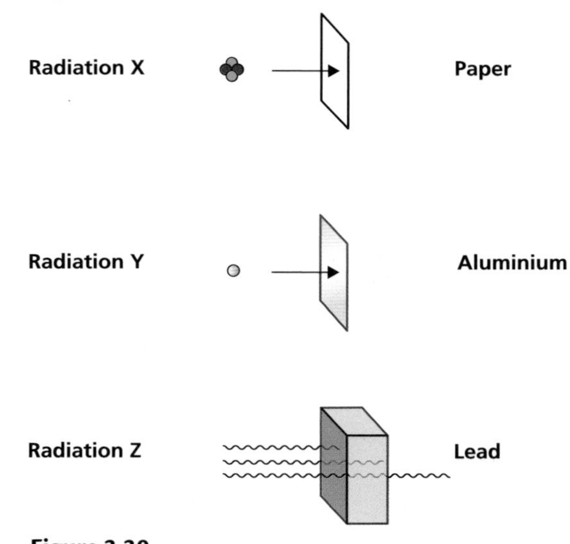

Figure 3.30

Which line in the table correctly identifies the types of radiation identified by particles X, Y and Z?

	Particle X	Particle Y	Particle Z
A	Alpha	Beta	Gamma
B	Beta	Alpha	Gamma
C	Beta	Gamma	Alpha
D	Gamma	Beta	Alpha

3 An atom of ^{227}Th decays by alpha emission to produce an atom of ^{211}Pb. How many alpha particles were released to produce this lead atom?

A 1

B 2

C 3

D 4

4 Figure 3.31 shows the radioactive decay of sodium-24. What is the half-life of this sample?

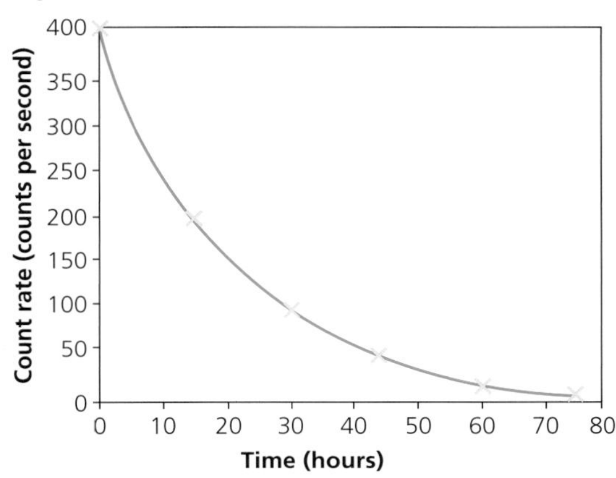

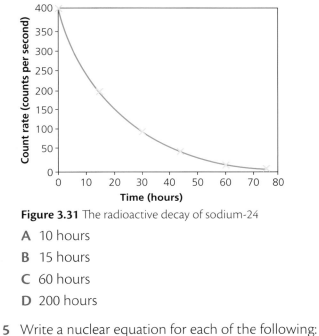

Figure 3.31 The radioactive decay of sodium-24

A 10 hours

B 15 hours

C 60 hours

D 200 hours

5 Write a nuclear equation for each of the following:

a) Alpha decay of Po-210

b) Beta decay of Sr-90

c) Alpha decay of Ra-226

6 A 200 g sample of radioactive iodine-131 was weighed accurately. Twenty-four days later the same sample was reweighed and only 16.375 g of the original sample remained. What is the half-life of iodine-131?

Chapter 3.5
Chemical Analysis

Chemists play an important role in society by monitoring our environment to ensure that it remains healthy and safe and that pollution is tackled as it arises. In this section we will revise how chemical analysis involves the identification and quantification of a chemical that may be present as a pollutant.

Chemical analysis can be put into two categories:

- Qualitative analysis gives an indication of the identity of a chemical in a sample.
- Quantitative analysis determines the amount of a chemical in a sample.

There are several methods that chemists use for analysis.

Qualitative (What is present?)	Quantitative (How much is present?)
Flame tests Can be used to identify metals present in a sample. Blue-green flame indicates presence of copper.	**Acid/Base titrations** Can be used to calculate the concentration of an acid or alkali present in a sample (see Unit 1).
Precipitation Can be used to determine ions present in a sample.	**Gravimetric analysis** Involves the accurate weighing of a precipitate to determine mass present.
Chromatography Can be used to identify a substance present in a sample.	

Answers

Chapter 1.1

1 A

2 C

3 a)

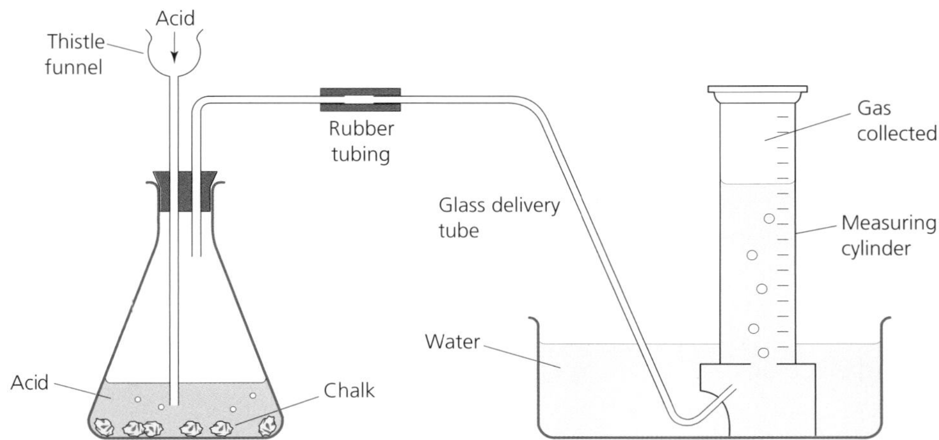

b)

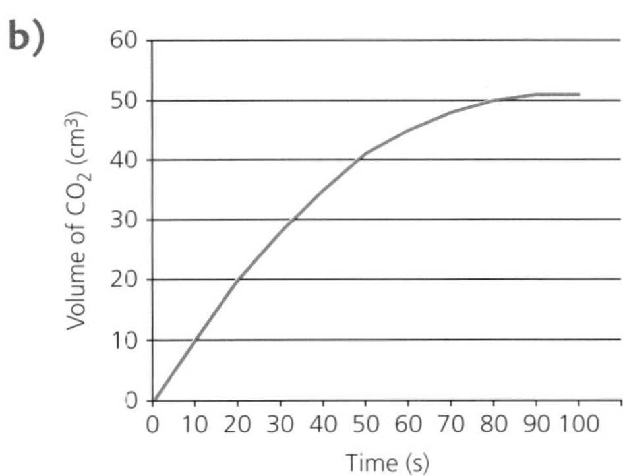

c) 0.875 $cm^3\ s^{-1}$

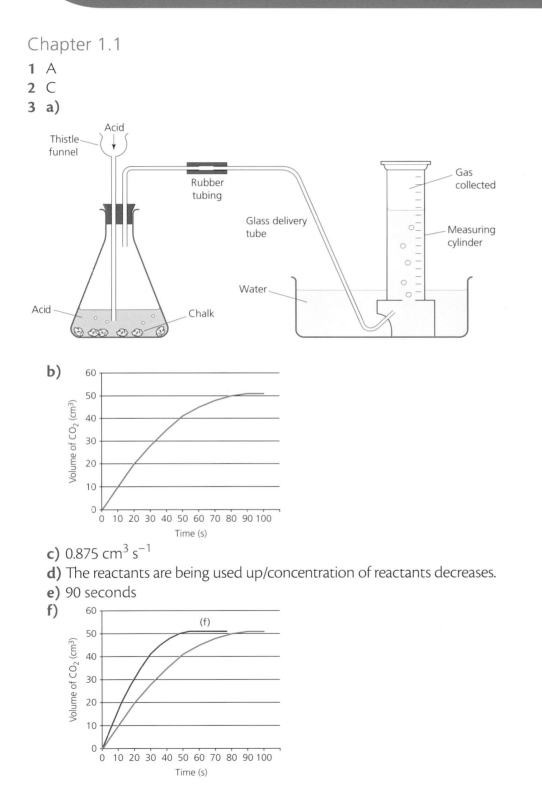

d) The reactants are being used up/concentration of reactants decreases.

e) 90 seconds

f)

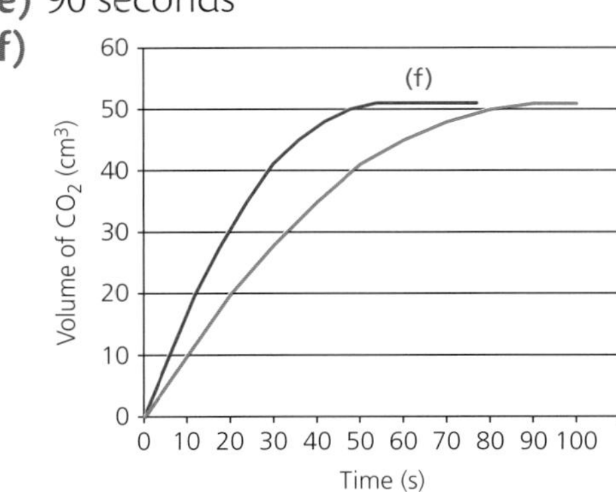

4 Small particle size results in a large surface area, therefore making the catalyst more efficient.

5 a) Liver = 2.15 $cm^3\ s^{-1}$, potato = 0.9 $cm^3\ s^{-1}$ (approx.)
   b) Liver
   c) Volume, temperature and concentration of the reactants.
      The particle size of the catalyst.

Chapter 1.2

1 A
2 A
3 B
4 C
5 a)

Particles	Number
Protons	47
Electrons	46
Neutrons	60

   b) Isotopes
   c) There is an equal amount of both isotopes.

6 a) $^{41}_{20}Ca$
   b) 20 protons and 21 neutrons
   c) Equal numbers of protons and electrons

Chapter 1.4

1 C
2 A
3 C
4 C
5 A
6 a) A covalent bond is a shared pair of electrons between two non-metal elements. The positive nuclei of each atom have an attraction for the shared electrons creating the bond.
   b)

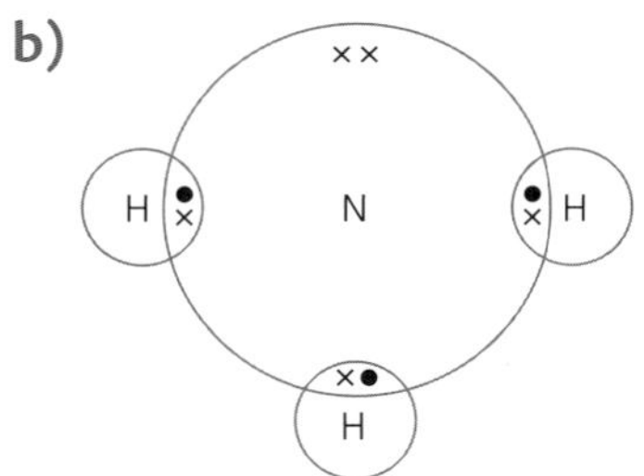

   c)

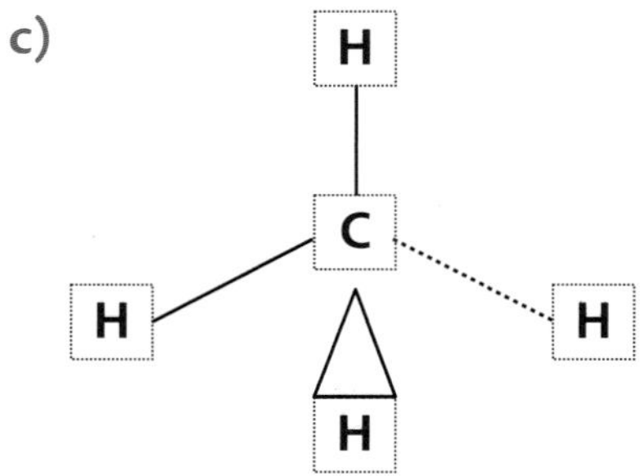

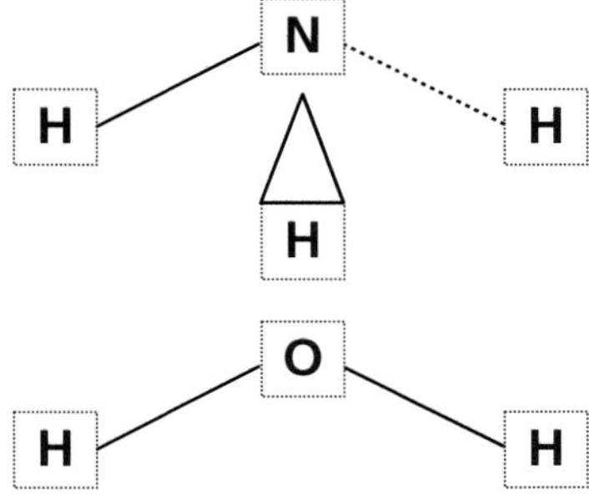

d) Water can form additional bonds between molecules which increase the boiling point of water.

7

Substance	Bonding and structure
D	Metallic
C	Ionic
B	Covalent network
A	Covalent molecular

Chapter 1.6

1 a) i. MgO **ii.** $CaCl_2$
iii. Al_2S_3 **iv.** NaF
v. $Ca(NO_3)_2$ **vi.** $(NH_4)_2SO_4$
b) i. $Mg^{2+}O^{2-}$ **ii.** $Ca^{2+}(Cl^-)_2$
iii. $(Al^{3+})_2(S^{2-})_3$ **iv.** Na^+F^-
v. $Ca^{2+}(NO_3^-)_2$ **vi.** $(NH_4^+)_2SO_4^{2-}$
c) i. 40.5 **ii.** 111
iii. 150 **iv.** 42
v. 164 **vi.** 132

2 a) $2Mg + O_2 \rightarrow 2MgO$
b) $CH_4 + 2O_2 \rightarrow CO_2 + 2H_2O$
c) $4Na + O_2 \rightarrow 2Na_2O$
d) $2Li + 2H_2O \rightarrow 2LiOH + H_2$
e) $4Fe + 3O_2 \rightarrow 2Fe_2O_3$
f) $N_2 + 3H_2 \rightarrow 2NH_3$

3 20 g

4 151.5 g

Chapter 1.7

1 C
2 A
3 B
4 D
5 C
6 B
7 a) *sodium oxide + water → sodium hydroxide*
b) $Na_2O + H_2O \rightarrow 2NaOH$
c) Greater than 7
d) Aluminium oxide is insoluble in water.
8 1 mol l^{-1}

Chapter 2.2

1 B
2 B
3 B
4 C
5 A
6 a) A family of hydrocarbons with similar chemical and physical properties that can be represented by a general formula.
b) CH_2O
7 a)

Hydrocarbon	Molecular formula	Observations on adding bromine solution	Saturated or unsaturated
A	C_5H_{10}	Remains brown	Saturated
B	C_5H_{10}	Brown to colourless	Unsaturated
C	C_5H_{12}	Remains brown	Saturated
D	C_5H_8	Brown to colourless	Unsaturated

b)

```
          H   H   H   H
H\        |   |   |   |
  C = C — C — C — C — H
H/            |   |   |
              H   H   H
```

c) Isomers

Chapter 2.3

1 B
2 C
3 A
4 B
5 a)

```
    H   H   H
    |   |   |
H — C — C — C — H
    |   |   |
    H   O   H
        |
        H
```

b) Propan-1-ol **c)** 0.01 moles

6 a)

```
    H   O       H   H
    |   ||      |   |
H — C — C — O — C — C — H
    |           |   |
    H           H   H
```

b) Ethanol **c)** Condensation/Esterification

7 a)

```
       O
      //
H — C
      \
       O — H
```

b) Ethanol

c)

```
    H   H       O
    |   |       ||
H — C — C — O — C — H
    |   |
    H   H
```

Chapter 2.5

1 A
2 D
3 **a)** Exothermic reaction **b)** 52.1 kJ (negative sign not required)
4 2006.4 kJ mol^{-1} (negative sign not required)
5 88 g
6 53.2 g

Chapter 3.1

1 A
2 A
3 A
4 B
5 C
6 B
7 B
8 A
9 B
10 **a)**

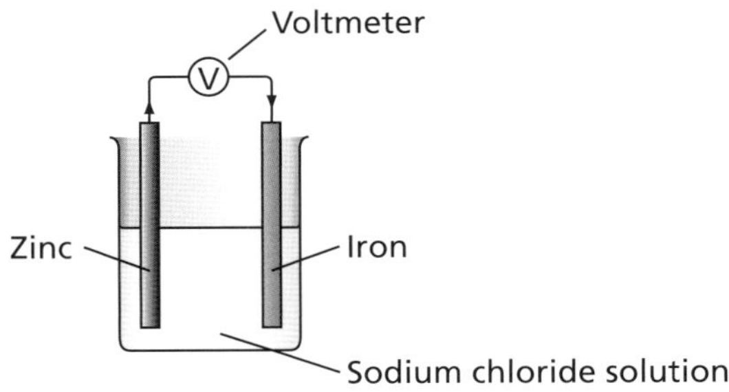

b)

Electrodes	Reading on voltmeter (V)	Direction of electron flow
Zn/Fe	0.3	$Zn \rightarrow Fe$
Zn/Al	−0.1	$Zn \leftarrow Al$
Zn/Ni	0.5	$Zn \rightarrow Ni$
Zn/Sn	0.7	$Zn \rightarrow Sn$

11 **a)** To provide oxygen **b)** Magnesium – zinc – copper
12 **a)** Displacement/redox
b) Nitrate
c) Silver is less reactive than copper.
d) $Cu \rightarrow Cu^{2+} + 2e^-$

Chapter 3.3

1 **a)** & **b)**

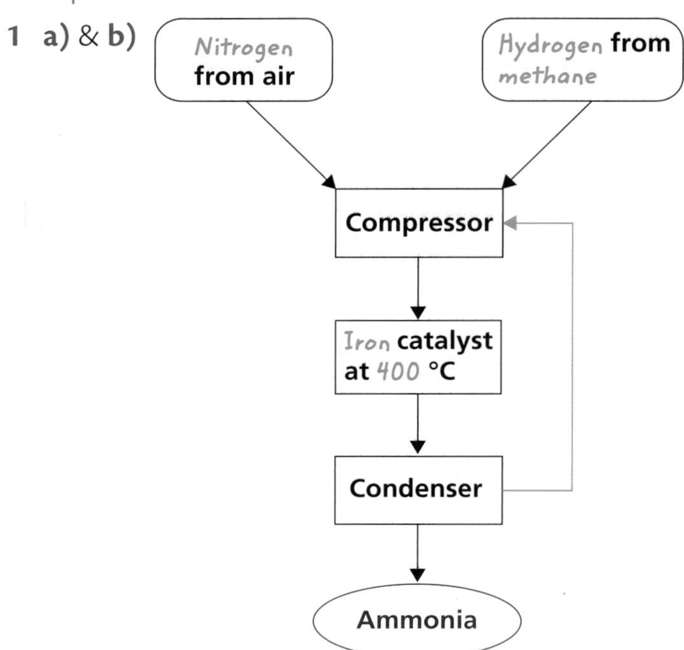

2 Condensation (polymerisation)

3 **a)** Man-made

b) Thermoplastic/thermosoftening plastic

4 **a)** Addition polymerisation

b)

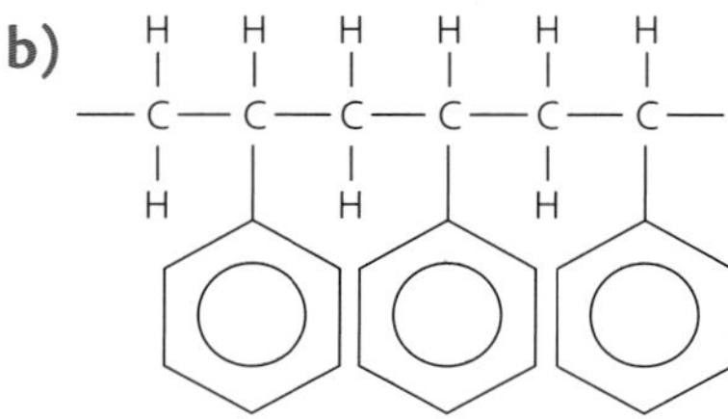

5 **a)** 28% **b)** 21%

6 **a)** $NH_4Cl(aq) + NaOH(aq) \rightarrow NH_3(g) + NaCl(aq) + H_2O(l)$

$NH_4^+(aq) + Cl^-(aq) + Na^+(aq) + OH^-(aq)$

$\rightarrow NH_3(g) + Na^+(aq) + Cl^-(aq) + H_2O(l)$

b) Ammonia has a lower density than air.

Chapter 3.4

1 B

2 A

3 D

4 B

5 **a)** ${}^{210}_{84}Po \rightarrow {}^{206}_{82}Pb + {}^{4}_{2}He$

b) ${}^{90}_{38}Sr \rightarrow {}^{90}_{39}Y + {}^{0}_{-1}e^-$

c) ${}^{226}_{88}Ra \rightarrow {}^{224}_{86}Rn + {}^{4}_{2}He$

6 8 days

Key words

Acid A substance with a pH below 7. They contain a higher concentration of H^+ ions than pure water.

Addition polymerisation A reaction in which many small monomers combine to form one large polymer molecule.

Addition reaction A reaction in which a small molecule, usually a diatomic molecule, adds across the double bond of an alkene.

Adsorption The temporary attachment of reactant molecules to the active sites of a catalyst.

Alkali A substance with a pH above 7 because it has a higher concentration of OH^- ions than pure water.

Alkali metals The very reactive group 1 metals.

Alkanes The simplest homologous series of saturated hydrocarbons with the general formula C_nH_{2n+2}.

Alkanoic acids A homologous series which contain the functional group –COOH on an end carbon. Also known as carboxylic acids.

Alkanols A homologous series which contains the –OH functional group. More commonly known as alcohols.

Alkenes A homologous series of hydrocarbons that are unsaturated and have the general formula C_nH_{2n}. They are isomers of the cycloalkanes.

Alpha particle Slow moving, positively charged particles that come from the nucleus of a radioactive element.

Atom A particle made up of protons, neutrons and electrons.

Atomic number The number given to each element in the periodic table. It is equal to the number of protons in an atom.

Base A soluble metal oxide that when dissolved in water produces an alkaline solution.

Beta particles Fast moving, negatively charged particles.

Biodegradable A substance that can rot away naturally.

Blast furnace The method by which iron is extracted from its ore.

Carbohydrates A food group that contains carbon, hydrogen and oxygen and provides energy for the body.

Carboxyl group The group –COOH found in carboxylic acids (alkanoic acids).

Carboxylic acids A homologous series which contain the functional group –COOH on an end carbon. Also known as alkanoic acids.

Catalyst Alters the rate of a reaction but is not used up in the reaction.

Catalytic converter Part of the exhaust system of a car that converts harmful gases into less harmful gases using a catalyst.

Cell Used to produce electrical energy from chemical energy.

Chromatography A separation technique that separates a mixture of liquids.

Compound A substance made up of two or more elements chemically joined.

Condensation polymerisation A type of polymerisation that produces a polymer and water. Starch is a condensation polymer.

Covalent bond A shared pair of electrons between two non-metals.

Covalent molecule A group of atoms held together by covalent bonds.

Covalent network A giant network of atoms held together by covalent bonds. They have very high melting and boiling points.

Cycloalkanes A homologous series with a ring of carbon atoms. They have the general formula of C_nH_{2n}. They are isomers of the alkenes.

Diatomic compound A compound with molecules containing two atoms only, such as carbon monoxide (CO).

Diatomic element An element whose molecules contain two atoms, such as chlorine (Cl_2).

Displacement reaction When a metal ion is displaced from a solution by a metal that is higher in the reactivity series.

Distillation A separation technique that separates a mixture of liquids with different boiling points.

Electrolysis The separation of an ionic solution using a DC power supply.

Electrolyte An ionic solution which conducts electricity.

Electron A negatively charged particle that has a mass of approximately 0.

Element A substance that contains only one type of atom.

Endothermic A reaction which takes in energy. This results in a decrease in temperature.

Enzyme A biological catalyst. They work best at body temperature.

Esters Compounds containing the –COO functional group. They are formed by a condensation reaction between an alcohol and a carboxylic acid.

Evaporation The process in which a liquid is turned into a gas by heat. It can also be used as a separation technique.

Exothermic A reaction that gives out energy. This results in a temperature increase.

Fermentation The process using yeast that turns sugar and water into alcohol and carbon dioxide.

Filtrate The liquid that passes through the filter paper and is collected after filtration.

Filtration A separation technique that separates an insoluble solid from a liquid.

Fuel A substance that reacts exothermically with oxygen.

Functional group The part of a molecule that gives the compound its chemical properties.

Gamma High energy wave emitted from the nucleus of an unstable atom.

Gram formula mass The mass of one mole of a substance.

Haber process The industrial method of ammonia production using an iron catalyst.

Half-life The time taken for the activity or mass of a radioactive element to drop by half.

Halogens The reactive non-metals in group 7 of the periodic table.

Heterogeneous catalyst A catalyst that is in a different state to the reactants.

Homogeneous catalyst A catalyst that is in the same state as the reactants.

Homologous series A family of compounds with similar chemical and physical properties that can be represented by a general formula.

Hydrocarbon A compound made up of carbon and hydrogen.

Hydroxyl group The functional group of alcohols (alkanols).

Ion A charged particle formed by the losing (metals) or gaining (non-metals) of electrons.

Ion bridge Used to complete the circuit in a cell.

Ionic bond The electrostatic force of attraction between a positive metal ion and a negative non-metal ion.

Ionic lattice A large arrangement of ions held together by ionic bonds. They have high melting and boiling points and dissolve in water. They conduct when molten or in solution.

Isomers Compounds with the same molecular formula but a different structural formula.

Isotope Atoms with the same atomic number but different mass numbers.

Mass number Equal to the number of protons plus neutrons in an atom.

Mole The formula mass of a substance.

Molecule Two or more atoms held together by covalent bonds.

Neutralisation The reaction of an acid with an alkali or a base that moves the pH towards 7.

Neutron A particle in an atom which is found in the nucleus and has a mass of 1 but no charge.

Noble gas Very unreactive non-metals found in group 8 of the periodic table.

Nucleus The positively charged centre of an atom that contains the neutrons and protons.

Ore The state in which a metal is found in nature.

Ostwald process The industrial method of nitric acid production from ammonia using a platinum catalyst.

Oxidation reaction A reaction in which electrons are lost.

Particle A subatomic constituent of the atom, such as an electron or proton.

pH A number that indicates the acidity or alkalinity of a substance.

Polymer A very large molecule formed by the addition of many small monomer molecules.

Polymerisation The reaction in which a polymer is formed by combining many monomers.

Proton A small, positively charged particle found in the nucleus of an atom. It has a mass of 1.

Reactivity series A list of metals (and hydrogen) in order of reactivity.

Redox reaction A reaction in which both oxidation and reduction take place.

Reduction reaction A reaction in which electrons are gained.

Relative atomic mass (RAM) The average mass of all the isotopes of an element.

Residue The insoluble solid left over in the filter paper after filtration.

Salt A product of neutralisation in which the hydrogen ion of an acid has been replaced by the ammonium ion or metal ion of the alkali.

Saturated hydrocarbon A hydrocarbon that has only single carbon to carbon bonds. Alkanes and cycloalkanes are saturated.

Spectator ion Ions that are present during a reaction but remain unchanged by the reaction.

Standard solution A solution which can be known and accurately measured.

Thermoplastic A plastic that will soften on heating and can be reshaped.

Thermosetting plastic A plastic that doesn't soften on heating.

Titration An analytical technique involving accurate measuring of volumes of reacting liquids.

Unsaturated hydrocarbon A hydrocarbon that contains at least one carbon to carbon double bond. The alkenes are unsaturated.

Valency The number of bonds that an element or ion can form.